Nuffield Primary Science
SCIENCE PROCESSES AND CONCEPT EXPLORATION

Materials

Key Stage 2

TEACHERS' GUIDE

PUBLISHED FOR THE NUFFIELD–CHELSEA CURRICULUM TRUST BY COLLINS EDUCATIONAL

NUFFIELD PRIMARY SCIENCE
Science Processes and Concept Exploration

Directors
Paul Black
Wynne Harlen

Deputy Director
Terry Russell

Project members
Robert Austin
Derek Bell
Adrian Hughes
Ken Longden
John Meadows
Linda McGuigan
Jonathan Osborne
Pamela Wadsworth
Dorothy Watt

Published 1993 by CollinsEducational
An imprint of HarperCollins*Publishers*
77–85 Fulham Palace Road
London W6 8JB

ISBN 0 00 310050 2

Printed and bound in Hong Kong

Design by Carla Turchini
Illustrations by Hemesh Alles, Gay Galsworthy, Maureen Hallahan, Helen Herbert, Sally Neave, Karen Tushingham, Joanna Williams
Cover artwork by Karen Tushingham

Programmes of Study and Attainment Targets from *Science in the National Curriculum (1991)* are Crown copyright.

Photograph acknowledgements
Page 22: Sally and Richard Greenhill
Pages 44–5: Arctic Camera (Richard Sale and Tony Oliver)
Page 60: David Phillips
Page 61: Frank Lane Picture Agency

Commissioned photography by Oliver Hatch

The Trust and the Publishers would like to thank the governors, staff and pupils of Hillbrook Primary School, Tooting, for their kind co-operation with many of the photographs in this book.

Safety adviser
Peter Borrows

Contents

Explanation of symbols in the margins

 Warning

 Good opportunities for work related to Attainment Target 1 (Science 1)

 Notes which may be useful to the teacher

 Vocabulary work

 Opportunities for children to use information technology

 Equipment needed

 Reference to the pupils' books

CHAPTER 1

Introduction

1.1 The SPACE approach to teaching and learning science

A primary class where the SPACE approach to science is being used may not at first seem different from any other class engaged in science activities; in either, children will be mentally and physically involved in exploring objects and events in the world around them. However, a closer look will reveal that both the children's activities and the teacher's role differ from those found in other approaches. The children are not following instructions given by others; they are not solving a problem set them by someone else. They are deeply involved in work which is based on their own ideas, and they have taken part in deciding how to do it.

The teacher has, of course, prepared carefully to reach the point where children try out their ideas. She or he will have started on the topic by giving children opportunities to explore from their own experience situations which embody important scientific ideas. The teacher will have ensured that the children have expressed their ideas about what they are exploring, using one or more of a range of approaches – from whole class discussion to talking with individual children, or asking children to write or draw – and will have explored the children's reasons for having those ideas.

With this information the teacher will have decided how to help the children to develop or revise their ideas. That may involve getting the children to use the ideas to make a prediction, then testing it by seeing if it works in practice; or the children may gather further evidence to discuss and think about. In particular, the teacher will note how 'scientific' children have been in their gathering and use of evidence; and should, by careful questioning, encourage greater rigour in the use of scientific process skills.

It is essential that the children change their ideas only as a result of what they find themselves, not by merely accepting ideas which they are told are better.

By carefully exploring children's ideas, taking them seriously and choosing appropriate ways of helping the children to test them, the teacher can move children towards ideas which apply more widely and fit the evidence better – those which are, in short, more scientific.

You will find more information about the SPACE approach in the Nuffield Primary Science *Teachers' handbook.*

1.2 Useful strategies

Finding out children's ideas

This guide points out many opportunities for finding out children's ideas. One way is simply by talking, but there are many others. We have found the following strategies effective. How you use them may depend on the area of science you are dealing with. In Chapter 3 you will find examples of these strategies, with suggestions as to where you might use them. More information about them is given in the *Teachers' handbook*.

Talking and open questioning

Whole class discussions can be useful for sharing ideas, but they do not always give all children a chance to speak. It is often helpful if children are allowed to think of their own ideas first, perhaps working them out in drawings, and are then encouraged to share these with others – perhaps with just one other child, or with a larger group.

Annotated drawings

Asking children to draw their ideas can give a particularly clear insight into what they think. It also gives you a chance to discuss the children's ideas with them. Words conveying these ideas can then be added to the drawing, either by you or by the child. Such work can be kept as a permanent record.

Sorting and classifying

This can be a useful way of helping children to clarify their ideas and to record their thinking. They could sort a collection of objects or pictures into groups.

Writing down ideas

Children may instead write down their responses to questions you pose. Writing gives children the opportunity to express their own views, which can then be shared with others or investigated further.

Log books and diaries

These can be used to record changes over a longer investigation. They need not necessarily be kept by individual children, but could be kept by a whole group or class. Children can jot down their ideas, as words or drawings, when they notice changes, recording their reasons for what they observe.

Helping children to develop their ideas

Letting children test their own ideas

This will involve children in using some or all of the process skills of science:

- observing
- measuring
- hypothesizing
- predicting
- planning and carrying out fair tests
- interpreting results and findings
- communicating

It is an important strategy which can, and should, be used often. The *use* of process skills *develops* them – for example, through greater attention to detail in observing, more careful control of variables in fair tests, and taking all the evidence into account in interpreting the results.

Encouraging generalization from one context to another

Does an explanation proposed for a particular event fit one which is not exactly the same, but which involves the same scientific concept? You or the children might suggest other contexts that might be tried. This might be done by discussing the evidence for and against the explanation, or by gathering more evidence and testing the idea in the other context, depending on children's familiarity with the events being examined.

Discussing the words children use to describe their ideas

Children can be asked to be quite specific about the meaning of words they use, whether scientific or not. They can be prompted to think of alternative words which have almost the same meaning. They can discuss, where appropriate, words which have special meaning in a scientific context, and so be helped to realize the difference between the 'everyday' use of some words and the scientific one.

Extending the range of evidence

Some of the children's ideas may be consistent with the evidence at present available to them, but could be challenged by extending the range of evidence. This applies particularly to things which are not easily observed, such as slow changes; or those which are normally hidden, such as the insides of objects. Attempts to make these imperceptible things perceptible, often by using secondary sources, help children to consider a wider range of evidence.

Getting children to communicate their ideas

Expressing ideas in any way – through writing, drawing, modelling or, particularly, through discussion – involves thinking them through, and often rethinking and revising them. Discussion has a further advantage in that it is two-way and children can set others' ideas against their own. Just realizing that there are different ideas helps them to reconsider their own.

1.3 Equal opportunities

The SPACE approach to teaching and learning science gives opportunities for every child to build on and develop his or her experiences, skills and ideas. It can therefore be used to benefit pupils of all kinds and at any stage of development. This is fully discussed in the *Teachers' handbook*.

1.4 Materials and the National Curriculum

This teachers' guide is divided into three themes; in each one there is a section on finding out children's ideas, examples of ideas children have, and a section on helping children to develop their ideas.

Programmes of study	Statements of Attainment
Pupils should investigate a number of different everyday materials, grouping them according to their characteristics. Properties such as strength, hardness, flexibility, compressibility, mass ('weight'), volume, and solubility should be investigated and related to everyday uses of the materials. ... Pupils should test the acidity and alkalinity of safe everyday solutions such as *lemon juice* using indicators which may be extracted from plants, such as *red cabbage*. Pupils should know about the dangers associated with the use of some everyday materials including hot oil, bleach, cleaning agents and other household materials.	2a) be able to group materials according to observable features. 3a) be able to link the use of common materials to their simple properties. 5b) be able to classify aqueous solutions as acidic, alkaline or neutral, using indicators.
Pupils should be given opportunities to compare a range of solids, liquids and gases and recognize the properties which enable classification of materials in this way.	4a) be able to classify materials as solids, liquids and gases on the basis of simple properties which relate to their everyday uses.
Experiments on dissolving and evaporation should lead to developing ideas about solutions and solubility. [Pupils] should explore ways of separating and purifying mixtures such as muddy water, salty water and ink, by using evaporation, filtration and chromatography. Pupils should explore the origins of a range of materials in order to appreciate that some occur naturally while many are made from raw materials. They should investigate the action of heat on everyday materials resulting in permanent change: these might include cooking activities and firing clay. Pupils should explore chemical changes in a number of everyday materials such as those that occur when mixing Plaster of Paris, mixing baking powder with vinegar, and when iron rusts. They should recognize that combustion of fuel releases energy and produces waste products including gases.	2b) know that heating and cooling everyday materials can cause them to melt or solidify or change permanently. 3b) know that some materials occur naturally while many are made from raw materials. 4b) know that materials from a variety of sources can be converted into new and useful products by chemical reactions. 4c) know that the combustion of fuel releases energy and produces waste gases. 5a) know how to separate and purify the components of mixtures using physical processes. 5c) understand that rusting and burning involve a reaction with oxygen.

Nuffield Primary Science Themes

Properties and use of materials

This theme provides opportunities for children to investigate a wide variety of everyday materials, their uses and their properties. Children tend to identify the properties of an article rather than the materials it is made from and frequently only refer to the characteristics that can be observed directly. The links children make between the properties and uses of materials are many and varied but rarely show any pattern. The activities encourage children to examine different materials closely and to identify the different properties each substance has. Detailed observations are used in the grouping of materials into various categories. Testing and measuring materials for properties such as strength, hardness, and flexibility further children's experiences of materials.

Solids, liquids and gases

This theme specifically explores the nature of solids, liquids and gases and the distinctions between these three forms of matter. Many young children do not use the terms solid, liquid or gas spontaneously but they tend to describe things using words such as 'metal', 'powder', and 'wood'. Ideas about solids and liquids are more clearly expressed than about gases, but in all cases there are difficulties in characterizing what makes a solid a solid, a liquid a liquid, and a gas a gas. The activities introduce children to a wide range of substances and encourage them to identify the properties that all solids, liquids, or gases have. The effects of heating substances causing them to change from solid to liquid to gas are introduced. Further development of the causes of such changes are explored in the *Using energy* teachers' guide, pages 36 – 41.

Changing materials

This theme considers two aspects of changing materials. The first is the changes which are brought about when particular materials are mixed together or treated in a particular way. Children are introduced to processes such as dissolving, filtration, chromatography, and to changes which bring about a permanent change in the materials. The second is the manufacture of materials and products. Many young children accept things as they are and that to change one thing into another is not possible except by 'magic'. Older children recognize the possibility of some changes but often with conditions. The activities help children investigate different ways of changing materials and tracing the manufacture of a range of products.

1.5 Attainment Target 1

Two important aspects of children's learning in science are:

◆ learning how to investigate the world around them;
◆ learning to make sense of the world around them using scientific ideas.

These are reflected in the National Curriculum. Attainment Target 1 'Scientific investigations' is about the first aspect, and the other attainment targets are about the second aspect. The weighting proposed for Key Stages 1 and 2 is 50 per cent for AT1 and 50 per cent for the others; this indicates the importance attached to scientific investigations at the primary stage.

Although these two aspects of science learning are specified separately in the National Curriculum, they cannot be separated in practice and it is not useful to try to do so. Through investigation children explore their ideas and/or test out the ideas which arise from discussion. As a result, ideas may be advanced, but this will depend on the children's investigation skills. Thus it is important to develop these skills in the context of activities which extend ideas. So there is no separate Nuffield Primary Science teachers' guide on scientific investigations, because opportunities to make these occur throughout all the guides and they form an essential part of the SPACE approach.

Thus in this guide you will find investigations which provide opportunities to develop the skills and understanding set out in AT1.

 These are marked in the text by the symbol shown here. In this teachers' guide, the investigations which cover the most skills are 'Testing materials' (page 37) and 'Materials in use' (page 43), 'Mixing and dissolving substances' (page 73) and 'Separating materials' (page 74).

It is important that teachers give active guidance to pupils during investigations to help them work out how to improve the way in which they plan and carry out their investigations.

Attainment Target 1 sets out three main areas in which children's skills should be developed, as follows:

i   'ask questions, predict, and hypothesize'. In this area, children should be helped to make progress from asking general and vague questions, to suggesting ideas which could be tested. Teachers' discussions with pupils should aim to help them to develop the skill of formulating a hypothesis, based on their scientific knowledge, in such a way that it can be tested in further experiments.

ii 'observe, measure, and manipulate variables'. Children's observations should become more relevant and more useful as they develop better ideas of what they are looking for and why. When children describe their observations, teachers may have to help them to improve them, for example by reminding them of what they are looking for. Such help should also encourage progress from qualitative comparisons and judgements to appreciating the value of making quantitative measurements (for example 'cold water' is qualitative; 'water at 12°C' is quantitative). This should lead to the development of skills with a variety of instruments and to increasing care and accuracy in measurement.

Similarly, when children describe the plans for their work, teachers should be helping them to develop a clearer understanding of the need to think about what is changing and being changed in an investigation (the variables) and of features which have to be kept the same in order to ensure a fair test (the controls).

iii 'interpret their results and evaluate scientific evidence'. Here children should be asked to think about and discuss what they have found out. As they learn to do so they should be careful in checking their evidence against the original ideas underlying an investigation and should become increasingly critical in discussing alternative explanations which might fit their evidence. In such discussions, children can often be given guidance to help see a need to conduct their investigation more carefully or in a different way.

In practice, children will not necessarily be predicting first, then observing and finally evaluating. Sometimes, observations may lead to questions and predictions, and interpretation of one piece of work can often lead to new questions and new measurements.

These three groups of skills, concerned with *asking questions, predicting and hypothesizing,* with *observing, measuring, and manipulating variables,* and with *interpreting results and evaluating evidence,* provide a framework for guiding children and assessing their progress in planning and carrying out investigations. The assessment example given in Chapter 4 is analysed with reference to these three aspects.

CHAPTER 2

Planning

2.1 Introduction: planning with children's ideas in mind

The key scientific ideas presented in this guide can be explored in various contexts, and many of the suggested activities can be incorporated into cross-curricular topic work. This chapter uses a worked example as an aid to planning a topic. Further information on planning is given in the Nuffield Primary Science *Teachers' handbook*.

A teacher using the SPACE approach should take into account:

◆ the need to find out children's own ideas, not only at the beginning of the work but also at intervals during it;
◆ the importance of planning the investigations with the children, using their ideas as the starting point;
◆ the concepts that are being explored;
◆ the direction in which the children's ideas are developing.

2.2 Cross-curricular topics

Activities which explore the ideas covered in this teachers' guide to *Materials* may be approached via a number of topics in addition to the one set out as an example in the planning sheets (pages 15–16). It is assumed that teachers will adapt the topic to whatever local resources are of interest and readily to hand. Some possibilities are given below.

Buildings and monuments

Houses in different times and places: architectural styles: medieval, Tudor, Regency, Victorian, 1930s; differing designs to suit local materials and needs.
Homes on water.
Homes for people who move from place to place.
Family homes and homes for an extended family.
Homes for shelter; homes for defence (castles and manor houses).
Shapes and patterns in houses.
Costing materials used for building.
Choice of materials for walls, for roofs, for windows, doors and flooring.

Some links with other Nuffield Primary Science teachers' guides and pupils' books include:

Forces and movement – use of tools, lifting and moving things, structures;
Rocks, soil and weather – rock types used for buildings, weathering effects on buildings;

Living things in their environment – organisms found living in and around buildings and monuments.

Clothes and fashion

Clothes worn in different countries: suitability for climate and customs.
Fashion.
Uniform.
Clothes in the past: changing styles and changing materials.
Clothes for different purposes: keeping warm, staying dry, keeping cool: which is the best material?
Clothes for protection: armour, space suit, underwater, sporting clothes, crash helmets, survival bags, mountaineering kit.
Raw materials: silk, wool, cotton, rubber, leather. How are they processed? Inventors and their role in the development of industries associated with these materials.
Man-made fibres: rayon, nylon. Where do they come from?
How do materials behave? Will wool stretch? How strong is cotton thread?
Footwear: measuring grip of different kinds of sole on different surfaces.
Wear and tear: effect of rubbing.
Protecting cloth: mothproofing, flameproofing and waterproofing.

Some links with other Nuffield Primary Science teachers' guides and pupils' books include:

Using energy – keeping warm or keeping cool;
Forces and movement – measuring grip of footwear;
The variety of life – sources of natural materials.

Furniture (and soft furnishings)

What materials should be used? Wood, metal, plastic, glass.
Changing design in furniture production.
Designs from different countries; beds in foreign lands.
Processes involved in manufacture: carving and joints.
Treatments: varnishing, polishing, painting, protection from insects.
Estimating amounts of materials needed for manufacturing an item.
Curtains, wall coverings (tiles, paper, paint) and floor coverings: advantages and disadvantages of different kinds of material for each purpose.
Wear and tear.
What is needed to stick wall and floor coverings?

Do it yourself!

Constructing and repairing things from models and paintings to cars and houses involves the selection of materials. What are the materials needed for? What is the best material to use for a particular job? Can alternative materials be used? Where do the materials come from? What has been involved in their manufacture?
Design and make an article from scratch.
Find out the types of tools that have been used to carry out particular jobs: how have the tools changed?

Some links with other Nuffield Primary Science teachers' guides and pupils' books include:

Electricity and magnetism – construction of electrical devices;
Forces and movement – use of tools;
Using energy – materials for draught-proofing.

Rubbish

How much rubbish is thrown away at school and/or at home?
What sort of materials are there in the rubbish?
Look at ways of reducing the rubbish: how much could be recycled or reused?
Do a litter survey (handle litter with gloves). Which materials decay and which remain?
Design a means of sorting rubbish for recycling: separating things which are magnetic, metal, wood, paper, plastic, etc.
How do different types of rubbish decay?

Some links with other Nuffield Primary Science teachers' guides and pupils' books include:

Electricity and magnetism – identifying magnetic materials;
Living things in their environment – decay of materials, reuse and/or recycling of waste materials;
The Earth in Space – rubbish orbiting the Earth.

Other topics

There are many parts of the home in which the materials present can be considered.

The kitchen provides foods, cutlery and other utensils.
The changes that can take place to common materials like water, salt, sugar and milk (cream, butter, cheese) can be considered.
Historical elements can be introduced: medieval and Victorian kitchens.
Staple diets in different countries can be looked at.
The bathroom, garden shed and garage provide a range of different materials. The bathroom, for example, provides ceramics, cleansers and cosmetics.

2.3 Topic plan examples

The following plans illustrate how the science related to *Materials* may be embedded in a cross-curricular topic. The topic presented is 'Buildings and monuments' and opportunities for exploring mathematics, language, history, geography, design technology and art have been indicated on the first plan. On the second plan the science work has been amplified to illustrate possible areas of exploration based within the overall topic, and relevant statements of attainment are shown. It is important to remember these are only examples and are not intended to be exhaustive.

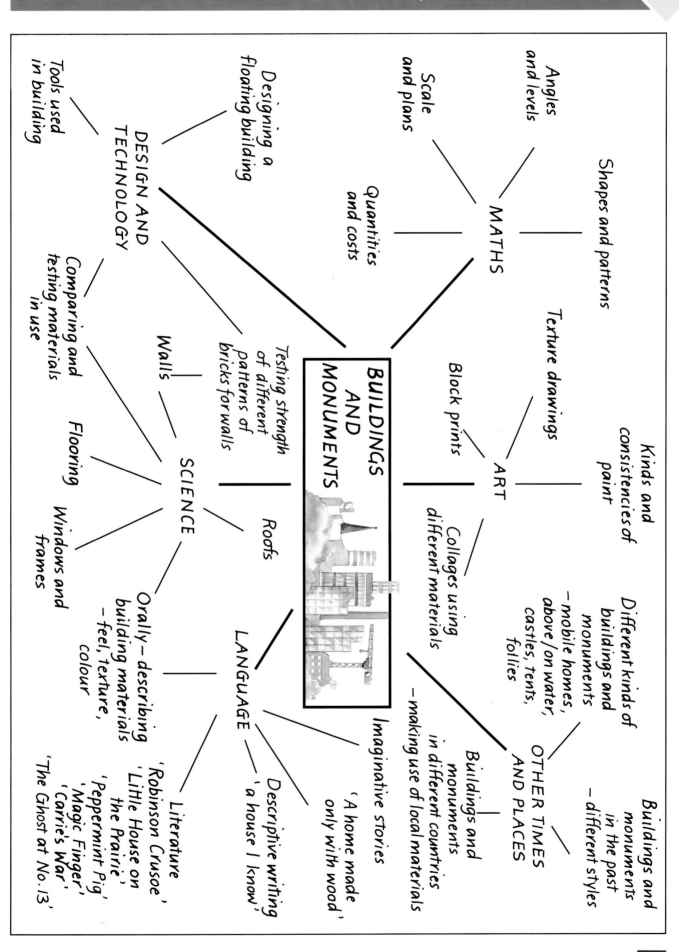

MATHS

Angles and levels

Scale and plans

Quantities and costs

Shapes and patterns

DESIGN AND TECHNOLOGY

Tools used in building

Designing a floating building

Comparing and testing materials in use

Walls

Flooring

SCIENCE

Testing strength of different patterns of bricks for walls

Roofs

Windows and frames

Orally – describing building materials – feel, texture, colour

LANGUAGE

Literature
'Robinson Crusoe'
'Little House on the Prairie'
'Peppermint Pig'
'Magic Finger'
'Carrie's War'
'The Ghost at No.13'

Descriptive writing
'a house I know'

Imaginative stories
'A home made only with wood'

Buildings and monuments in different countries – making use of local materials

OTHER TIMES AND PLACES

Buildings and monuments in the past – different styles

Different kinds of buildings and monuments – mobile homes, above/on water, castles, tents, follies

Collages using different materials

ART

Kinds and consistencies of paint

Texture drawings

Block prints

BUILDINGS AND MONUMENTS

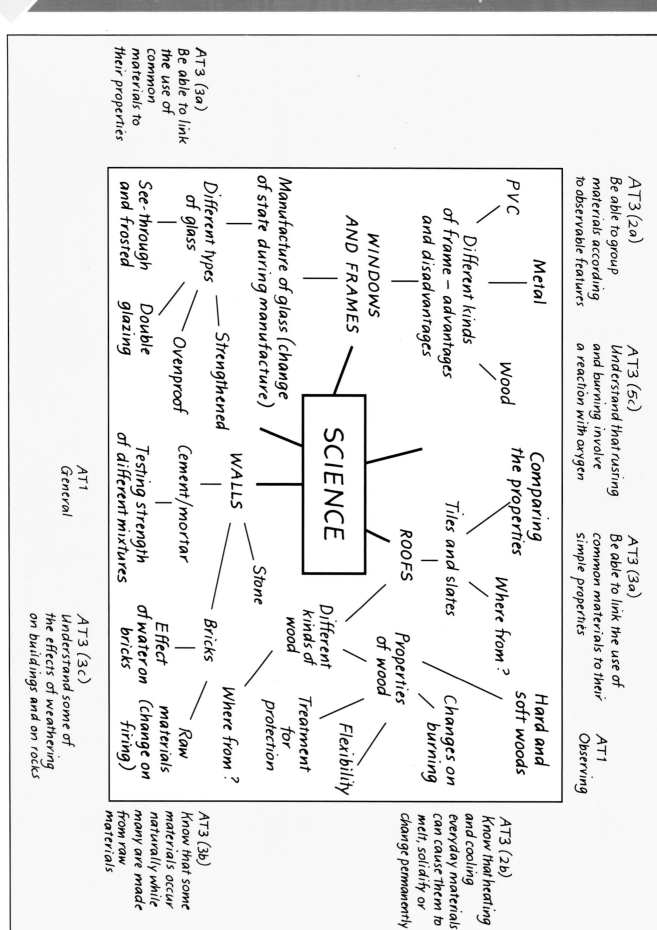

AT3 (3a)
Be able to link
the use of
common
materials to
their properties

AT3 (2a)
Be able to group
materials according
to observable features

AT3 (5c)
Understand that rusting
and burning involve
a reaction with oxygen

AT3 (3a)
Be able to link the use of
common materials to their
simple properties

AT1
Observing

WINDOWS
AND FRAMES

PVC — Different kinds
of frame – advantages
and disadvantages

Metal

Wood

Different types
of glass — Strengthened

See-through
and frosted

Double
glazing

Ovenproof

Manufacture of glass (change
of state during manufacture)

SCIENCE

Comparing
the properties

Where from?

Hard and
soft woods

Tiles and slates

Changes on
burning

ROOFS

Properties
of wood

Different
kinds of
wood

Treatment
for
protection

Flexibility

WALLS

Cement/mortar

Testing strength
of different mixtures

Stone

Bricks

Where from?

Effect
of water on
bricks

Raw
materials
(change on
firing)

AT1
General

AT3 (3c)
Understand some of
the effects of weathering
on buildings and on rocks

AT3 (3c)
Understand some of
the effects of weathering
on buildings and on rocks

AT3 (3b)
Know that some
materials occur
naturally while
many are made
from raw
materials

AT3 (2b)
Know that heating
and cooling
everyday materials
can cause them to
melt, solidify or
change permanently

2.4 Use of information technology

 Specific examples of opportunities to use information technology are indicated by this symbol in the margin and referred to in the text. The examples include:

◆ word processing to produce reports of investigations;
◆ simple databases to record and analyse data collected, such as properties of a set of materials;
◆ use of a sensor coupled with a computer to detect and measure temperature.

2.5 Pupils' books

 References to relevant material in the pupils' books are given throughout Chapter 3. They are indicated in the margin with this symbol.

The pupils' books accompanying this guide are called *Materials* and *More about materials*. They provide useful secondary source material relating to *Materials* as well as background reading and starting points for discussions. They can be used to introduce or extend ideas included in this guide.

Here is a list of topics included in the pupils' books.

Materials
Disasters
Fighting fires
Gas and air at the fair
There's no place like home
Old gold and other metals
Keeping records
Materials for sculpture
Rotten things
Shovelling and pouring
What's in a lunch box?
A trip back in time

More about materials
Magic formulae
Anyone for tennis?
Fighting dirty
From clay to ceramic
Materials sayings
Touring a flavour factory
The case of the organized jewellery
A tale of two bicycles
Sorting out the waste problem
Solving paint's problems
A trip to Mars

You may also find the *Using energy*, *Habitats* and *Rocks, soil and weather* pupils' books useful.

2.6 Resources

Full use should be made of the school grounds, other areas of the local environment which are safely accessible, and places for appropriate visits if they can be arranged.

The precise nature of the resources needed at any time will, of course, depend upon the ideas that the children have and the methods of testing that they devise. However, the following list provides a general guide to the resources needed to carry out the investigations shown in this book.

Different kinds of everyday material found in the home, such as:

metals
ceramics
plastics
liquids
rubber
elastic
fabrics

Containers, including if possible, some transparent ones with lids

Tools and implements for testing materials, such as:

files
sieves
scissors
masses ('weights')
pliers
magnets
torches
sandpaper
hammers
nails
magnifying glasses
moulds
hacksaws

Things for holding and pouring materials, such as:

spoons
droppers

Glassware suitable for holding hot liquids (e.g. Pyrex)

Thermometers (see 'Warnings' below)

Safe equipment for heating: stubby candles or night lights in a metal tray of sand

Eye protection

Books, videos, pamphlets and other sources of information, particularly about the origin and manufacture of materials. Many firms may provide information about their products: for example, metals, rubber, plastics, wool, cotton, paper, bricks.

2.7 Warnings

 Activities which need particular care are indicated by this symbol in the margin. Everything possible should be done to ensure the safety of the children during their investigations. You should consult any guidelines produced by your school or LEA and if possible by CLEAPSS. See also the Association for Science Education publication *Be safe! some aspects of safety in school science and technology for Key Stages 1 and 2* (2nd edition, 1990). This contains more detailed advice than can be included here. In particular, it has detailed sections on tools, testing things, heating and burning and the kind of materials (chemicals) that are suitable or not suitable to use.

The points listed below require particular attention.

Unsuitable chemicals include:

bleach
caustic soda (sodium hydroxide)
de-rusting solutions
dishwasher detergents
disinfectants
dry cleaning fluids
some fertilizers
fireworks, sparklers, and party poppers
some plant growth substances, e.g. rooting powders
hydrogen peroxide
lavatory cleansers
'Milton' (hypochlorite solution)
oven cleaners
paint strippers
pesticides, fungicides, and insecticides
scale removers
weedkillers
biological and automatic machine washing powders.

Children should know how to use the tools which are available. Cutting implements should be kept sharp and warnings to take care should be given. Make sure that saw blades are firmly fixed to hacksaw handles and that materials are firmly secured to a bench before cutting. Craft knives should only be used under close supervision. Any hammers used should be small ones with heads that are firmly fixed.

Children should be aware of the potential danger from flying pieces when materials are being tested, especially when this is done to breaking point. There are dangers to the face and eyes when materials snap and eye protection should be considered. Care should be exercised when objects are allowed to fall. When attaching loads to a material, put a cardboard box of soft material underneath to cushion any fall.

Make sure that materials and equipment to be used in food preparation are not mixed up with those sometimes identical items which are to be tested in various ways. Warn children about the dangers of tasting unknown substances.

Some sources of heat such as spirit burners and portable bottled gas burners should not be used. For many purposes, hot water from a tap or kettle can provide a source of heat. If a direct local flame is needed, then stubby candles or night lights are suitable. These should be stood in a layer of dry sand inside a metal tray (such as a baking tray).

All heating should be done under close adult supervision. The eyes should be protected when necessary. Ensure that small amounts are used and that ventilation is adequate. Some materials including plastic produce harmful fumes and so materials for heating should be carefully selected (see the ASE book *Be safe!* for guidance on heating and on chemicals). Materials can be heated in metal spoons, spoons made of cooking foil, metal lids or bottle tops with the linings removed. While plastic containers are often useful for holding materials, ovenware or Pyrex glass should be used for hot liquids.

Care should be exercised if glass is broken. Broken glass should be wrapped in newspaper before disposing of it.

Avoid mercury-in-glass thermometers for temperature measurement. Thermal (liquid crystal) strips, spirit-filled, dial type and digital thermometers are all suitable.

Some chemicals can be safely used by children. (Any substance can be harmful, however, if taken in sufficient quantity.) Other chemicals require close adult supervision because they are poisonous, flammable, corrosive or irritant. Some household chemicals such as bleach and disinfectants should be used in the classroom only by the teacher, if at all. DO NOT assume that because something is easily available at home it must be safe. It is often NOT. (Lists of suitable and unsuitable chemicals are given in section 7 of *Be safe!* CLEAPSS produces similar but more extensive lists.)

CHAPTER 3

Exploring materials

Theme organizer

MATERIALS

PROPERTIES AND USES OF MATERIALS

3.1

There is a wide variety of materials, both natural and man-made, which differ in their properties.

Materials can be grouped according to their properties.

The uses of materials are related to their properties.

Materials can exist as solids, liquids or gases.

Materials can be changed into different forms.

SOLIDS, LIQUIDS AND GASES

3.2

Materials can exist as solids, liquids or gases.

Heating can change solid to liquid and liquid to gas; these changes can be reversed by cooling.

*Different forms of the same material have some different and some common properties.

*Materials are made up of particles.

*The differences between solids, liquids and gases can be explained in terms of the way in which particles are arranged.

CHANGING MATERIALS

3.3

Materials can be changed into different forms.

Some materials can be changed permanently by heating, but in other materials the changes can be reversed by cooling.

*Different forms of the same material have some different and some common properties.

*Some materials occur naturally but may be purified or processed before use; others are made by chemically changing the raw materials.

(*Asterisks indicate ideas which will be developed more fully in later key stages.)

Properties and uses of materials

AREAS FOR INVESTIGATION

Children should experience as wide a range of materials as possible and be encouraged to:

◆ describe materials in terms of their properties;

◆ compare and contrast different kinds of materials;

◆ group and classify materials according to their properties;

◆ carry out simple tests on a variety of materials;

◆ identify uses of materials and relate these to the properties of the materials in question.

KEY IDEAS

◆ There is a wide variety of materials, both natural and man-made, which differ in their properties.

◆ Materials can be grouped according to their properties.

◆ Materials can exist as solids, liquids or gases.

◆ The uses of materials are related to their properties.

◆ Materials can be changed into different forms.

A LOOK AT
properties and uses of materials

Although the word 'material' is often used to mean a fabric of some kind, it has a wider meaning that includes everything from which things are made, such as metals, ceramics, plastics, rubber, wood, glass, cement, leather, bone, textiles, glue, paints, skins, dyes, solvents, foodstuffs and medicines.

Some objects, such as cooking foil or erasers, are made of only one material. Others, such as buildings or ballpoint pens, are made of more than one material.

Each material has its own characteristics. Cement, for example, sets as a relatively hard, though brittle, solid. Rubber is softer and much more flexible. The characteristics of materials are often put in terms of opposites: hard or soft, strong or weak, stiff or bendy, and so on. Most characteristics (properties) of a material can be measured in more accurate terms.

Some materials have different forms, and the properties of these may vary. For instance, there are many different kinds of wood, some harder, some more flexible, than others; but they all have the general properties of wood and can be identified as such. Similarly, a particular type of steel may be harder than others but it is still steel.

The properties of a material make it suitable for particular uses. The transparency of glass makes it suitable for windows. Plastics are particularly useful materials because of the ease with which they can be shaped into different forms. A number of materials can often be used for the same thing. The choice of which is used will often be decided by what it costs and what it looks like.

NATIONAL CURRICULUM PROGRAMME OF STUDY

Pupils should investigate a number of different everyday materials, grouping them according to their characteristics. Properties such as strength, hardness, flexibility, compressibility, mass ('weight'), volume, and solubility should be investigated and related to everyday uses of the materials. ... Pupils should test the acidity and alkalinity of safe everyday solutions such as *lemon juice* using indicators which may be extracted from plants, such as *red cabbage*. Pupils should know about the dangers associated with the use of some everyday materials including hot oil, bleach, cleaning agents and other household materials.

Finding out children's ideas

■ STARTER ACTIVITIES

The activities described below provide opportunities for discovering children's ideas about most aspects of materials, their properties and their uses. Thus they provide starting points for wider investigations.

1 The variety of materials

A display of everyday materials provides an excellent starting point. Set up a collection of materials and ask children to provide additional items, thus increasing the variety. Examples of materials that might be included are shown below.

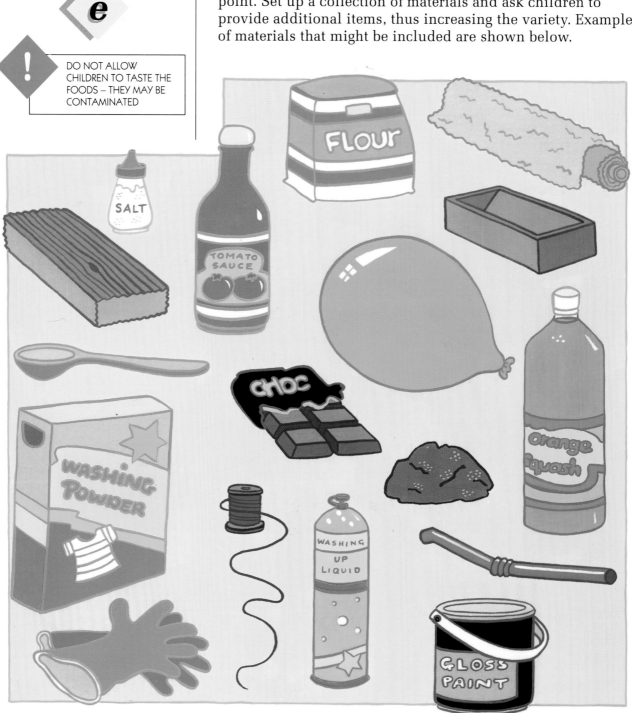

e

! DO NOT ALLOW CHILDREN TO TASTE THE FOODS – THEY MAY BE CONTAMINATED

Vary the composition of the display according to the experience of the children. At this stage no attempt should be made to group the items to reflect possible classifications of the materials. Similarly, words such as 'solid', 'liquid' and 'gas' should be avoided unless introduced by the children themselves. This is because we are trying to find out how the children refer to the materials and what words they use spontaneously.

Prompt children's thinking with questions set up beside the display. These might include:

 What do you know about each material?
What do you notice about each material?
What could you do to any of the materials to find out more?
Which things do you think should go together?
Which things do you think should be kept apart?

Encourage the children to record their informal responses to the questions, and any other comments they can make, in a class log book. This can be used as a basis for class discussions.

Alternatively, each child can keep an individual record, in words or pictures, about any of the items on the display. This could be done in a table with headings such as those shown here.

Material	What I can say about it	Date

Children might also be asked to put various materials into groups, giving reasons for their arrangements. Different groupings may then be discussed.

2 Finding out about materials

This activity could be carried out in conjunction with the display, or set up as an activity in its own right. Provide a variety of materials for children to test, such as water, flour, kitchen foil, paper, rubber, piece of rock, block of wood, cotton fabric, spoon. The materials should be accompanied by a range of 'implements' which might include:

water and containers
file
sandpaper
scissors
moulds (perhaps of sand)
spoons
torch
sieves
hammer and nails
pair of pliers
magnet
pestle and mortar
magnifying glass

AT 1 OBSERVING. CLASSIFYING

e

Items for heating or burning can be used, with great care. If heating materials in a flame, use very small amounts – only 2 or 3 strands of fibre 1 centimetre long, or 5-millimetre squares. You will need a wooden clothes peg attached to a stick to hold the material with, and a night-light or stubby candle in a metal sand tray.

 HEATING AND BURNING SHOULD BE DONE ONLY UNDER CLOSE ADULT SUPERVISION. DO NOT HEAT SUBSTANCES WHICH ARE HIGHLY FLAMMABLE, SUCH AS OIL, PLASTIC, OR PAINT, OR SUBSTANCES WHICH COULD BURN CHILDREN VERY BADLY, SUCH AS COPPER PIPE

 THIS ACTIVITY NEEDS CAREFUL SUPERVISION, SINCE CHILDREN MAY THINK OF UNEXPECTED AND DANGEROUS COMBINATIONS OF MATERIALS AND IMPLEMENTS

 OBSERVING. RECORDING

Invite the children to test various combinations of materials and implements, and ask them to find out what they can about the materials. They can record their 'tests' in words or pictures on a table such as that shown here.

Material	What I did	What I found out

Children's ideas about more specific aspects of the materials investigated can be found by asking various questions. For example, ideas about hardness and softness might be gleaned by drawing the child's attention to two items and asking:

Q *Which do you think is the harder material?*
What makes you say this is harder?
How could you find out if it was harder?
Why would you do it that way?

By using the same materials and repeating the questions but replacing 'harder' with 'stronger', it is possible to gain insights into how these two properties are distinguished, if at all. Ideas about other properties, such as mass ('does it feel heavy or light?'), flexibility and transparency, can be found out in the same way.

3 Comparing materials

Provide a selection of about six different materials for children to examine. Exactly what items you choose is less important than noting the features the children use to compare the materials. One set might consist of the items shown below.

For ease of handling these could be placed in clear screw-topped bottles (avoid glass bottles if possible).

Ask the children to:

◆ look at items carefully;
◆ choose two;
◆ say how the pair are alike;
◆ say how the pair are different.

TAKE CARE THAT CHILDREN DO NOT THROW IRON FILINGS AROUND, OR GET THEM IN THEIR EYES

AT 1   CLASSIFYING

This can then be repeated for another pair. Alternatively, one item can be chosen and compared with each of the others in turn. Charts of similarities and differences can then be drawn up and the outcomes discussed.

4 Relating materials to their use

Encourage children to think about what different objects are made from. This can be done either from the display of materials suggested in the first starter activity (page 24) or by a simple survey of everyday objects, both large and small. Ask questions such as:

 Why do you think steel is a good material for making bridges?
Why do you think glass is a good material for making windows?
Why do you think wool is a good material for jumpers?

Other examples of materials and objects might be:

metal for coins
white spirit for cleaning paintbrushes (flammable!)
rubber for tyres
wood for furniture.

By careful selection of the material and object you can focus on particular properties of materials, such as strength, hardness, solubility, transparency and flexibility.

Ask also why a material is not good for a particular use – for example:

 Why do you think rubber is not a good material for making bridges?

Children's ideas

Describing materials

Children describe things predominantly according to the uses of the item and other associations with which they are familiar. The following extracts show the range of responses children make when asked to describe various items.

Material	What can I say about it
Paint	Paint can be any colour. It is used for decorating things, there are different kinds of paint. Some are thick and some are thin.
plastic bag	This is used for carrying things in. It has two holes used for handles. It is dangerous to put one over your head.
washing up liquid	This is green. It is put in water and then bubbles come to the surface and the liquid takes the food and the stains of the plates, pots, cups and dishes.
Polish	Polish is used for cleaning and shining things. It comes in tins. Shoe polish is usually black. It is put on by a brush
Spoon	Spoons can be any size from a baby spoon to a table spoon. It can be used for eating breakfast, lunch, tea and anything else they can have round bits like the soup spoons and they can have decorations on them.

Water. Water is clear but some isn't you can have water deep or shallow it doesn't really matter you can have a handfull of water but it will just run out of your hands.

Materials	What I can say about it
A Brick	The Brick is hard It has a red couler It has holes in and it has abit of moss on and it stile has concreat.
oil	The oil is greenyellow it has a tin it comsout slowy in dreps

Some children describe materials in response to their own observations of a particular item. They often do not refer to properties they cannot observe in that example.

Date	Materials	What I can say about it
31:1:90	washing up Lequid	The washing up liquid smelles of lemon and feels oily the coulour is yellow

Other children are able to refer more generally to the properties of an actual material.

Water	It is a clear liquid. You can drink and you add it to some drinks. When it is frozen it becomes ice. When snow melts it becomes water. Rain is water. Water is in places like rivers streams and many other things like that

> Wood
>
> Wood can come in different shapes and size big or small it can be thick or thin long or short Square or round oblang triangler. It can be a different kind of wood oak and so on. Also it can be rough or smooth and it can be anything if you make something out of it.

Although there is often uncertainty about the actual words used to describe properties such as hardness and strength, some children can make a clear distinction, as in this example.

> Wood
>
> Its hard and can be any shape. Although its hard its quite easy to break. Some times piecies of it flake off. Wood starts off as a tree, but is cut down to make doors, cubords, etc. They can also be rough and smooth.

Comparing materials

Children of all ages tend to find identifying differences between materials much easier than identifying similarities, as this table shows. (The materials were given to the children in containers distinguished only by letters.)

	Alike	Different
A and B	none	One is heavier than the other and one in harder than the other.
A and C	none	One is darker than the other. One is heavier than the other.
A and D	none	A is darker and heavier than D.
A and E	none	When you shak E bubbles appear. When you shak A it makes a noies
B and C	none	C is heavier and darker than B.
B and D	They are both the same colour.	B is softer than D.
B and E	E makes a noies and B does not	

Many children try to identify the materials and to use this information in comparing items. However, they do not always appear to distinguish between the substance itself and its properties.

Pair of Conductes	ALIKE	DIFFERENT
A and C	I think a+B are alike as they are both Black	But are differet to as c is an acid wich is like black water and A is a metal
A and D	There is nothing the same about these	These two are different by the colour and A= metal + D= powder

Uses of materials

Various reasons may be given for the use of materials in particular situations, for example in terms of:

◆ functional properties

Wood is good because it won't collapse apart.

◆ manufacturing suitability

You nail it [wood] together and it sticks together.

◆ aesthetic properties

Wood looks nice if it's stained.

◆ and even economic grounds

> *Well, it's stronger really ... and I suppose it's the only thing about, because there are loads of trees which you can get wood off.*

Helping children to develop their ideas

The chart opposite shows how you can help children to develop their ideas from starting points which have given rise to different ideas.

The centre rectangles contain starter questions.

The surrounding 'thought bubbles' contain the sorts of ideas expressed by children.

The further ring of rectangles contains questions posed by teachers in response to the ideas expressed by the children. These questions are meant to prompt children to think about their ideas.

The outer ovals indicate ways in which the children might respond to the teacher's questions.

Some of the shapes have been left blank, as a sign that other ideas may be encountered and other ways of helping children to develop their ideas may be tried.

All the starter activities provide opportunities for helping children develop their ideas about materials. For most children the most important need is to extend their experience of the types of material that are found on the Earth. This can be done in three main ways:

♦ observing and describing materials;
♦ testing materials;
♦ investigating the uses of materials.

1 Observing and describing materials

The following activities provide an excellent opportunity to develop children's vocabulary as well as their observation skills and experience of materials. Two suggestions are made, but many variations are possible.

(You may also find the 'sayings' in *More about materials* useful for helping children to extend their vocabulary.)

a Unseen properties

Children should be blindfolded, or a piece of material should be placed in a 'feely' bag or box. Ask the children to use their senses of touch, smell, and hearing to describe and if possible to identify a range of materials.

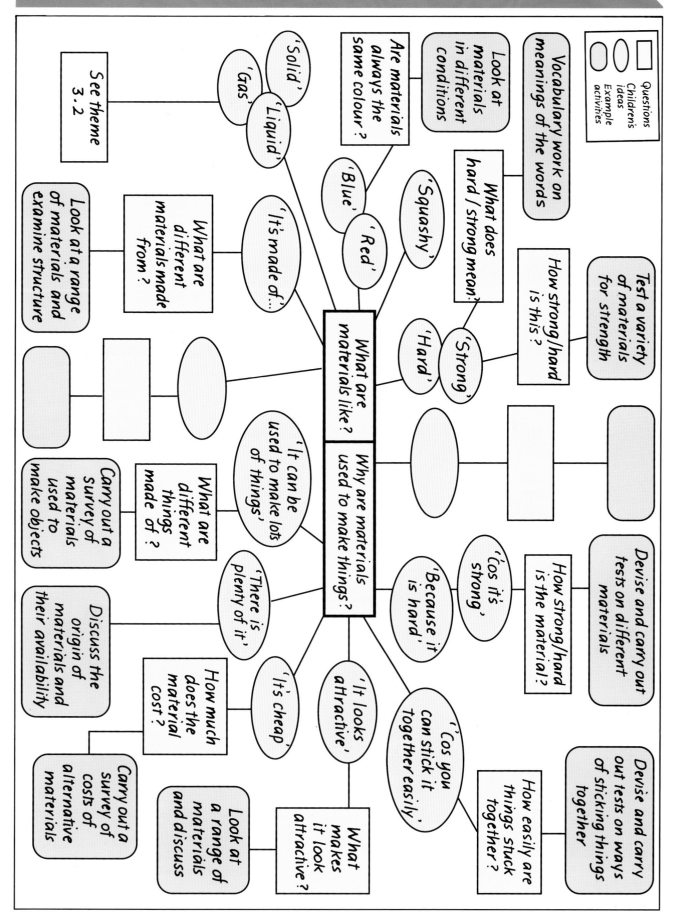

Questions
Children's ideas
Example activities

Vocabulary work on meanings of the words

Look at materials in different conditions

Are materials always the same colour?

'Solid'
'Gas'
'Liquid'
'Blue'
'Red'
'Squashy'

See theme 3.2

What does hard/strong mean?

What are different materials made from?

'It's made of...'

Look at a range of materials and examine structure

Test a variety of materials for strength

How strong/hard is this?

'Hard'
'Strong'

What are materials like?

Why are materials used to make things?

What are different things made of?

'It can be used to make lots of things'

Carry out a survey of materials used to make objects

'There is plenty of it'

Discuss the origin of materials and their availability

How much does the material cost?

'It's cheap'

'It looks attractive'

'Because it is hard'

''Cos it's strong'

How strong/hard is the material?

Devise and carry out tests on different materials

''Cos you can stick it together easily'

How easily are things stuck together?

Devise and carry out tests on ways of sticking things together

What makes it look attractive?

Look at a range of materials and discuss

Carry out a survey of costs of alternative materials

AT 1 — OBSERVING

Q *What does it feel like? Is it hard or soft, stiff or bendy? Does it have a smell? Can you think of anything that is like this material? What makes you say that it is ...?*

It is important that the children are encouraged to concentrate on what the material is, not on the object itself (for instance, that something is metal, not that it is a spoon). Where possible, use samples of material that are not made into particular objects.

b Guessing game

Can you bend it?

Is it metal?

Is it soft?

This activity can be done in pairs, in groups or as a class. One child is given a piece of material which the other children cannot see. She then describes the material, perhaps one feature at a time, and the other children attempt to guess what it is.

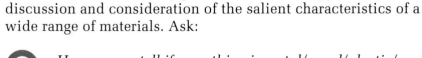

Alternatively, other children could ask questions about the material in an effort to identify it. Encourage them to start with general questions rather than to jump to conclusions.

In both forms this activity provides excellent opportunities for discussion and consideration of the salient characteristics of a wide range of materials. Ask:

Q *How can we tell if something is metal/wood/plastic/ rubber?*

t MATERIALS HAVE PARTICULAR PROPERTIES WHICH HELP TO IDENTIFY THEM

If children refer to solids, liquids and gases, or to the uses and origins of the materials, these topics can be followed up by using some of the activities described in 'Solids, liquids and gases' (page 44) or 'Where do materials come from?' (page 62).

Materials gives example of everyday materials which can be discussed. *More about materials* tells a story about identifying and sorting different materials (jewellery).

pb

2 Testing materials

There are many ways in which children can test materials. Each one provides opportunities for them to:

◆ devise an investigation;
◆ identify the relevant variables;
◆ make predictions;
◆ construct and carry out a fair test;
◆ make appropriate measurements;
◆ record their findings, e.g. in a table or chart;
◆ draw conclusions from their findings;
◆ communicate the outcome to others.

AT 1 GENERAL

The properties that might be investigated include strength, hardness, mass ('weight'), volume, transparency, solubility, flexibility, absorbency, compressibility, elasticity and plasticity. See 'Background science' for more information on these properties.

The starting point for many investigations will be the observations made by the children during the starter activities (pages 24–8).

> *This is the strongest string.*
> *The sponge is the softest thing here.*
> *You can see through plastic better than you can see through glass.*

Children's comments often need to be rephrased as questions which can then be investigated.

The following are examples of activities that groups of children can carry out during their investigations of materials.

Check pupils' plans before they start, bearing safety in mind.

a Which is the strongest?

While looking at clothes children may be asked which type of sewing 'cotton' is the strongest (in fact some sewing thread is synthetic). The following test could be set up to investigate this. Collect as many different makes of thread as possible, cut off equal lengths of each and fasten them to the apparatus shown above. 'Weights' are then attached to each piece of thread in turn until it breaks. The heaviest 'weight' that the thread can support is taken to be a measure of how strong it is. Place a waste-paper basket, filled with waste materials, underneath the 'weights' and collect them when the cotton breaks.

If anyone suggests that the strength may be tested by putting the same weight on all the threads and recording how long it takes for each one to snap, this could lead to further discussion.

Questions could include:

Q *What is the best way to measure the strength of cotton?*
Do both tests measure the same thing?
What do we mean by strength?
Why are some kinds of cotton stronger than others?

b Which material is the hardest/softest?

Children's responses to the starter activities often indicate some confusion over pairs of words such as 'hard/strong' and 'soft/smooth'. Therefore some discussion of what these words mean is an essential part of devising ways of testing materials for hardness and similar properties.

Children could test different materials by scratching samples with the point of a large nail. They could be asked:

 How can we make this a fair test?

The hardness of different kinds of wood could be tested by dropping an object such as a large ball bearing on to them. (Care!)

To help children devise and improve on their tests, questions may be asked such as:

 Why should the weight be dropped from the same height each time?
Why do you think it is important to use the same weight each time?

Ask also:

 What do you think makes some things hard and some things soft?
Do you think it is possible to make something hard/soft that is soft/hard to begin with?

c Stretching and bending materials

There are different ways of testing the 'stretchiness' and 'bendiness' of materials. Here is one example for 'stretchiness' and one for 'bendiness' which evolved from children's own designs.

'Stretchiness'

Children could stretch materials using the method shown here, and measure the increases in length. Ask:

 MEASURING

 PLANNING AND CARRYING OUT FAIR TESTS

Q *Why should each piece be the same length to start with?*
Why is it important to leave the weight on for the same length of time in each case?
What is the length of the material when the weight is taken off?
Do some materials go back to their original size?
How long does this take?

'Bendiness'

Measure the bend as the distance from the horizontal ruler to the tip of the material strip. Ask:

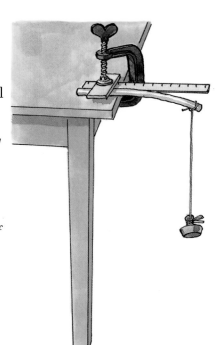

 MEASURING. PLANNING AND CARRYING OUT FAIR TESTS

Q *Which materials bend most easily?*
What happens if a heavier weight is used?
Can the 'bendiness' of something be changed? How might this be done?
Why do you think some materials are 'bendy'?

d Which material can we see through the best?

During the starter activities children may comment that it is possible to see through some materials but not others. This property could be further investigated in the following way.

Make a collection of transparent, translucent and opaque materials, including clear and coloured plastic and glass as well as different papers.

Get the children to group them into those which can be seen through easily, those which can be seen through a little and those which cannot be seen through. A chart or table could be used to show the groups.

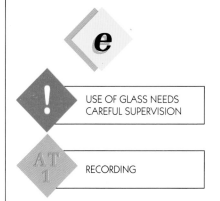

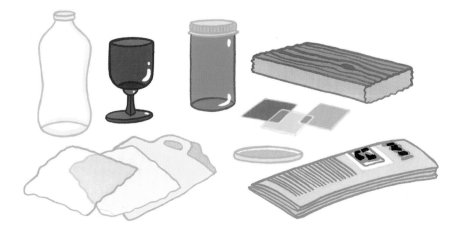

Discuss the qualities of the different groups of materials.

 Why can we see through some materials but not others? Can we devise a test to find out which material we can see through best?

One group of children drew a cross on a piece of white paper and viewed this through the different materials from varying distances. They scored how well they could see the cross using a scale 0 (could not see it) to 5 (could see it very clearly).

Discussion of their results raised further questions, such as:

 Does the distance between the object and the material make any difference?
What effect does the colour of the materials have on how well we can see through them?
Can we see through some coloured materials better than others?

USE OF GLASS NEEDS CAREFUL SUPERVISION

AT 1   RECORDING

AT
1
PLANNING AND
CARRYING OUT FAIR
TESTS

e What is the best material for mopping up water?

Children should be encouraged to think of ways in which this might be tested. The important factors to be taken into consideration are the amount of water to be mopped up, the size of the piece of material, and how it is used. All of these factors should be kept the same as far as is possible.

Children could spill some water on a tray and use a piece of material to mop it up. They should then count how many wipes are needed to dry the tray.

To test different materials, they could dip one end of a strip of material into water and then measure the height to which the water moves up the strip.

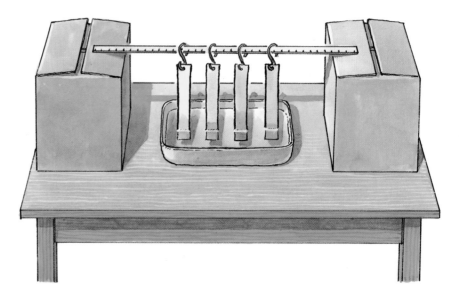

Discussion about mopping up water may lead children to consider the cleaning effects of water and other products. *More about materials* gives examples which may be used as part of the discussion.

3 Materials in use

Follow up children's responses to the starter activity (page 28) by asking them to identify the materials that have been used in making various objects. One approach would be a materials survey around the school.

Groups of children could work on particular materials. Ask:

Q *What is wood used for?*
What is plastic used for?
What is rubber used for?

Each group should try to:

- ◆ identify the material(s);
- ◆ collate all the uses of the material(s);
- ◆ suggest, and if appropriate test, how the use of the material(s) is related to its properties;
- ◆ relate the relevant properties to the identified uses of the material(s).

Such an activity provides opportunities for children to:

- ◆ plan investigations;
- ◆ identify patterns in their results;
- ◆ devise and carry out fair tests;
- ◆ use secondary sources actively;
- ◆ discuss and communicate their findings.

AT 1   GENERAL

Each group of children could present its findings as a wall display including charts and tables.

A class discussion of all the findings will help to identify general patterns of use of materials.

Another approach would be to use *More about materials* as a starting point for discussing the different painted surfaces which children see about them and on their journey to school. What different painted surfaces can they think of? Why are they painted? Is the paint lasting well? Children with bicycles may like to see whether the paint has successfully prevented rust.

pb

! SOME OLD PAINTS CONTAIN LEAD, WHICH IS TOXIC. AVOID HANDLING THEM

Such discussion could be extended by considering the use of materials in other situations. *Materials* and *More about materials* give some examples for consideration.

Materials gives some examples of how materials used in the wrong conditions can lead to disaster.

Solids, liquids and gases

AREAS FOR INVESTIGATION

◆ Looking at and describing different kinds of solid and liquid.

◆ Measuring and weighing solids and liquids.

◆ Finding examples of gases, and investigating events in which gases are involved.

The activities given in 'Hot and cold' in the Teachers' guide *Using energy* consider the processes which convert materials from solid to liquid and liquid to gas, and vice versa. It is worth considering whether to combine these two themes.

KEY IDEAS

◆ Materials can exist as solids, liquids or gases.

◆ Heating can change solid to liquid and liquid to gas; these changes can be reversed by cooling.

◆ *Different forms of the same material have some different and some common properties.

◆ *Materials are made up of particles.

◆ *The differences between solids, liquids and gases can be explained in terms of the way in which particles are arranged.

(*Asterisks indicate ideas which will be developed morefully in later key stages.)

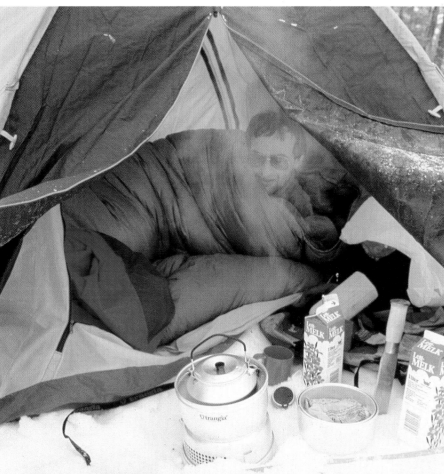

A LOOK AT
solids, liquids and gases

Materials normally exist in a particular state – solid, liquid or gas.

Solids are not always hard. Some, such as cotton wool or sponge, are soft, and others, such as talcum powder or flour, are powders. All solids have a definite shape. Even though a powder spreads out and pours like a liquid, each grain of it has a particular shape. Similarly, soft solids have a shape which can easily be changed by pressing.

The shape of a liquid can be determined by the kind of container it is in. When poured, it will spread out.

Gases also have no fixed shape but, unlike liquids, will keep spreading out until they completely fill the space they are contained in.

Heating can change a solid to a liquid or a liquid to a gas, while cooling reverses the process.

Finding out children's ideas
■ STARTER ACTIVITIES

1 Use of the terms 'solid' and 'liquid'

To see if children use the words 'solid' and 'liquid' spontaneously, you can ask them to compare pairs of materials taken from the display used in the starter activity in 'Properties and uses of materials' (page 24). Suitable examples are given below.

Take two solids and ask:

Q *How do you think these two are alike?*
How do these two differ from one another?

Repeat for a pair of liquids and then for a solid taken with a liquid. An alternative to using materials from the display is to place materials in transparent sample containers.

Ask the children to compare, for example:

◆ two relatively hard materials such as wood and stone;
◆ something hard with something softer, such as a piece of cloth or Plasticine;
◆ two relatively 'thin' liquids such as vinegar and diluted orange cordial;
◆ a 'thicker' liquid such as glycerine with a 'thin' liquid;
◆ a transparent solid such as plastic with a transparent liquid (water).

Children might give their ideas about similarities and differences orally or they could write them down, perhaps in a table. This activity is also an opportunity to assess whether (and with which characteristics) they compare materials.

2 Ideas about solids, liquids, and gases

Are they alike or different?

Is this a solid, a liquid or a gas?

Ask the children to draw pictures of solids, liquids, and gases on a sheet of paper divided into three.

Where the word appears to mean nothing to the child that section can be left blank. The drawing could be labelled to make it clear what is being represented, and further items can be listed if there are a lot of ideas.

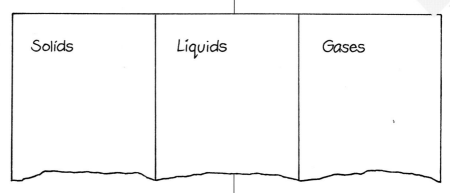

Solids	Liquids	Gases

3 Classifying examples of solids and liquids

Children can be shown a number of sealed transparent containers each containing a different material. These could be a hard solid, a soft solid, a 'bendy' solid, a powdery solid, a 'thin' liquid and a 'thick' liquid.

 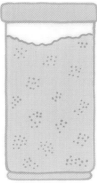    

Then ask them:

 Which do you think are solids?
How did you decide?
Which do you think are liquids?
How did you decide?

If any are left over, they can be asked:

 What about ...? What do you think that is?

This activity might be done through discussion with individuals or with the members of a small group, each giving their own opinions.

! CHILDREN MUST NOT BE
ENCOURAGED TO SNIFF
UNKNOWN SUBSTANCES

4 Further ideas about gases and liquids

a Smelling

Ask the children to open a container of vinegar and carefully smell it.

Show children how to sniff a substance safely: point the container away from the face and use a hand to waft the vapour towards the nose. Warn them *not* to take a deep breath. Do not use anything other than vinegar.

Q *How are you able to smell the vinegar?*
What happens when you smell the vinegar?

The children can make annotated drawings to show their ideas.

b An 'empty' container

Show the children an 'empty' transparent container, then put its lid on. Ask:

Q *Some people say that this is not empty. Why do you think they say that?*

If the children do not mention air, you could ask:

Q *Do you think there's any air inside it?*

Further questions about air might follow, such as:

Q *What can you tell me about air?*
Where can you find air?
What do you think air is?
Do you think air weighs anything? What gives you that idea?
Do you think air is a gas? What makes you say that?

The children could give oral or written responses.

c A colourless liquid

Show the children an unlabelled transparent container of colourless liquid (use water). Ask:

 What do you think this could be?
What else might it be?
How could somebody find out whether it is water or not?
Why might it be dangerous to have something unlabelled like this at home?
Do you think all liquids have got water in them?
Can you think of any that don't? What about milk?

Again, oral or written replies might be sought.

This may be a good opportunity to teach children why it is dangerous to taste unknown substances.

Label the container, or dispose of the liquid, immediately after use. Do not leave unlabelled containers lying around.

WARN CHILDREN TO TAKE CARE WITH UNKNOWN LIQUIDS

d Fizzy drinks

After looking at fizzy drinks children might be asked:

 What do you think the bubbles are?
What is happening to the bubbles?
Where do the bubbles come from?

Similar questions might be asked for other examples where bubbles are found in liquids (soapsuds) or solids (Aero chocolate, expanded polystyrene).

SOME *LEAS* DO NOT PERMIT YOUNGER CHILDREN TO HANDLE EXPANDED POLYSTYRENE

Children's ideas

'Solid', 'liquid' and 'gas' are not terms which many children use spontaneously. A lump of metal, for example, is more likely to be described as 'metal' than as 'solid'. When children are asked to give examples of solids, or of hard and strong materials, they often mention metals, and very seldom give examples of soft and powdery solids.

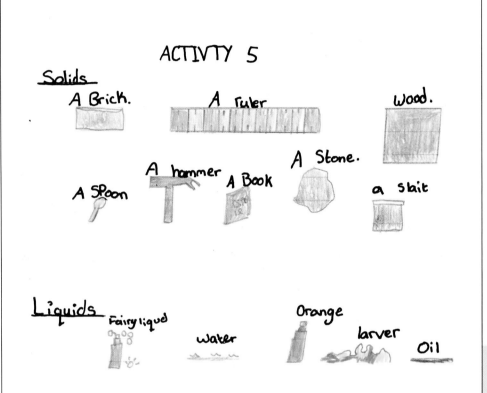

ACTIVTY 5

Solids
A Brick. A ruler Wood.
A Spoon A hammer A Book A Stone. a shit

Liquids Fairy liqud Orange
water larver Oil

Gas

Gas fiear

This picture not only illustrates the kind of solids that children think of, but also indicates that children are likely to give fewer examples in responding to the words 'liquid' and 'gas'. This may partly be because children focus on the words themselves and think only of examples containing them: washing-up liquid, gas cooker. Certainly when given a thin liquid like water or vinegar, children readily categorize it as liquid. Thicker liquids such as treacle may not be so readily classified.

It's not a liquid because it looks sticky.

When asked to put materials into the categories 'solid', 'liquid', or 'neither', children are likely to vary in their response to soft and powdery solids.

That's a material [cotton wool] and that's a powder [talcum powder]. Flour's a liquid 'cos you can pour it.

Solids are often characterized as hard and/or strong. In contrast, children focus on various characteristics of liquids.

> Liquids are like a drink, they're wet.
> If you shake it, it just goes like that ... all the bubbles.
> There's always a flat surface no matter where you lean them.
> You can pour liquids.

Colourless liquids are often treated as if they were water. Indeed, some children believe that a colourless liquid could be nothing else but water. This may lead them to suggest potentially dangerous tests.

> I'd drink it to see if it tastes like water.

Non-aqueous liquids (not containing water) are not often referred to. On the other hand, children may believe that some aqueous liquids, such as milk, do not contain water.

Gases are often difficult to perceive and so, not surprisingly, may cause more difficulty to children than either liquids or solids. There may be a tendency to focus on gas used at home for heating and cooking, and hence to associate gases with danger. When children were asked what they could say about gases, they said:

> Gas is usually in a bottle and stuff comes out and gas comes with it.
>
> Flame comes out. Sometimes when we open it it sometimes smells ... and then we just close it. They're all hot ... they smell horrible and they can kill you.

Occasionally smoke may be confused with gas.

> Smoke from chimneys. That's a gas.

Gas and vapour are not often mentioned when talking about smelling.

> Teacher   How do you think you smell the vinegar?
>
> Child   You smell it because it's strong. The smell goes up your nose.

Air may be accepted as a gas even by those for whom it does not readily come to mind when asked for examples of gases. Here are some different ideas about air.

Air is something you can't feel and it's everywhere.

It doesn't weigh anything because when you have a scale and you leave it the air is in the dish but it doesn't go down.

There's only air in the room if the doors are open a bit. Air needs to be around you because it makes you breathe more easily.

Helping children to develop their ideas

The chart on the next page shows how you can help children to develop their ideas from starting points which have given rise to different ideas.

The centre rectangles contain starter questions.

The surrounding 'thought bubbles' contain the sorts of ideas expressed by children.

The further ring of rectangles contains questions posed by teachers in response to the ideas expressed by the children. These questions are meant to prompt children to think about their ideas.

The outer ovals indicate ways in which the children might respond to the teacher's questions.

Some of the shapes have been left blank, as a sign that other ideas may be encountered and other ways of helping children to develop their ideas may be tried.

'Hot and cold' in the *Using energy* teachers' guide (pages 36–41) contains many suggestions for encouraging children to develop their ideas about changes of state from solid to liquid and liquid to gas, and vice versa. The activities here focus on the properties of solids, liquids and gases, and children's understanding of these terms.

1 Solids and liquids

a Liquids display

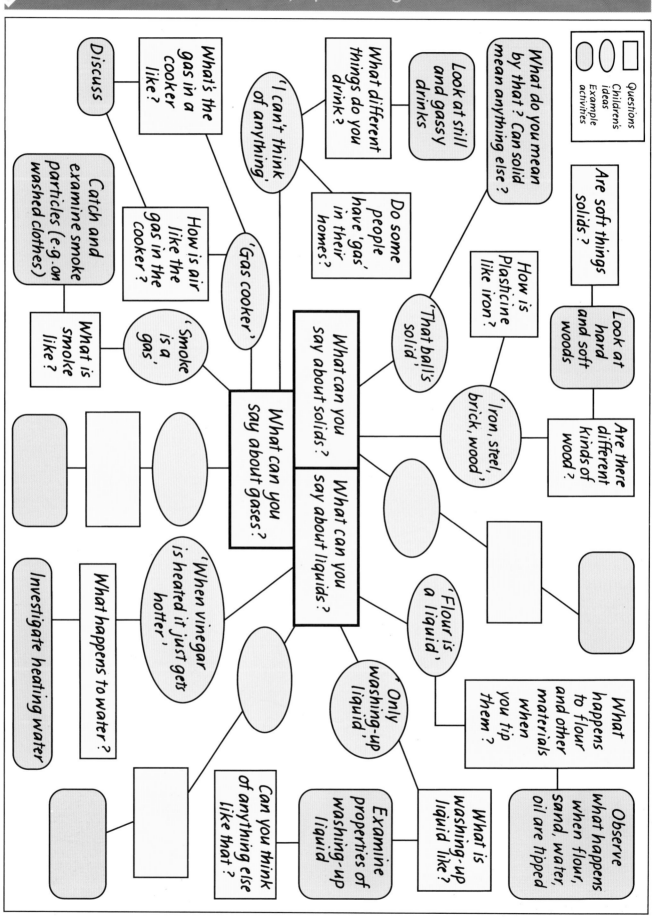

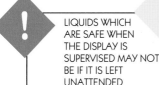
Ask children to think of as wide a variety of liquids as possible. These might be displayed, using real materials where these are safe and available, and pictures where they are not. Suitable liquids for display are fizzy drinks, glycerine, lemon juice, milk, oil, tea, and vinegar. This is an opportunity to discuss why some liquids cannot be left lying around safely.

LIQUIDS WHICH ARE SAFE WHEN THE DISPLAY IS SUPERVISED MAY NOT BE IF IT IS LEFT UNATTENDED

Children might talk about the examples in the display. Ask them:

Q *What do all the liquids have in common?*

Encourage children to develop descriptive words for liquids rather than forming any exact definition. Help discussion with further questions.

Materials can be used as the basis of a discussion about what a liquid is.

Q *Are all liquids colourless?*
How are liquids different from one another?
Do all liquids have water in them?

Children's own observations may be enough to respond to the first two questions, but they will probably need to use secondary sources for the third.

Children can be helped to appreciate that water can be present in a coloured or opaque liquid by being asked to try to dissolve various coloured materials in water – for example, orange drink crystals and coffee granules. This offers an opportunity to undertake investigations of solubility such as those described in 'Origins and manufacture of materials' (page 73).

b Solids display

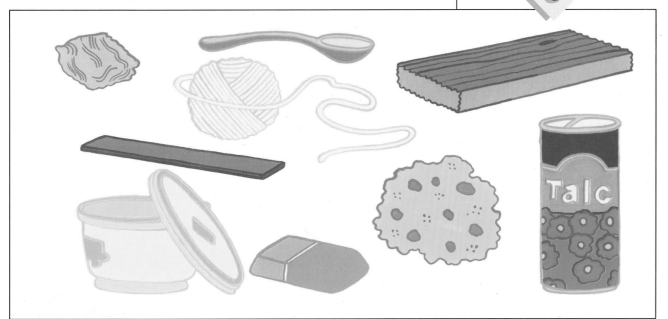

3.2

Make a display of solids, using both real materials and pictures. Real materials could include blackboard chalk, moist clay, soap, steel wool, a piece of wood, and a stone. Examples of soft and powdery solids such as sponge and talcum powder should be included.

Pose questions to stimulate discussion and enquiry by the children:

Q *Do you think all these things are solids?*
Is this (soft material) a solid?
Is this (powder) a solid?
What do all the solids have in common?

In some cases you may need to ask whether there are any exceptions to what seem to be the common properties of the solids. The following questions may also help children focus on the meaning of the term 'solid'.

Q *Are there different kinds of solid?*
What makes some solids seem different?
Can solids be put into groups?

Children might also be ready to discuss how 'solid' might have different meanings in different contexts.

Q *Does the word 'solid' always mean the same thing?*

Some children use the word 'solid' to describe a table or iron bar, when they actually mean hard or rigid. They may not consider talcum powder to be solid.

More about materials compares an ordinary Mars bar with a Mars ice-cream bar. This could provide a starting point for discussion of different kinds of solid. Some children could consider the temperatures at which the fat in different kinds of chocolate melt – have they noticed that milk chocolate melts in the mouth more quickly than plain chocolate? This is because butter, the fat from milk, melts at a lower temperature than cocoa butter, the fat which comes from the seed of a cocoa plant. This could form a link with *Using energy*.

More about materials lists sayings which children could use to discuss the meanings of different words related to materials (solids, liquids and gases).

c Comparing solids and liquids

Children could be asked to compare liquids with solids. They could place different materials in transparent sample containers and put the lids on tightly. Suitable materials are sand, sugar, pebbles, washing up liquid, oil, treacle, milk.

They should then tip the containers and observe what happens to the contents.

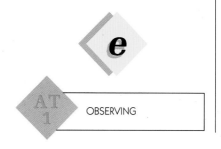

OBSERVING

Questions to ask could include:

 What happens to the liquids when the container is tipped? Do any solids do the same? What happens to the other solids? Which materials change shape when they are tipped?

Seeing that both liquids and powdery solids pour and change shape could lead to a discussion of what distinguishes them.

In their discussion one class gathered together a box of gravel, granulated sugar, icing sugar and wet and dry sand. They tried to pour each of these materials, and agreed that all could be poured but some flowed further than others. They also agreed that the gravel and granulated sugar were definitely solids and that the sand and icing sugar could be made up of very small solid bits. Examination with a hand lens showed this to be so.

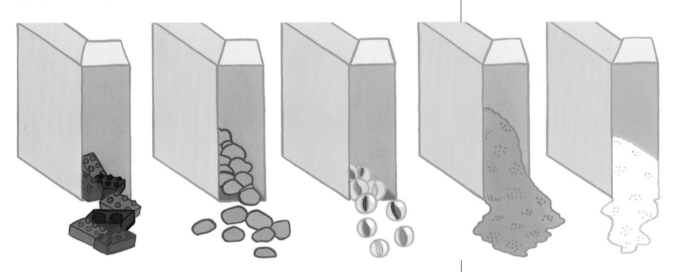

Soft solids may also change shape as they fall. What differentiates them from liquids? Children can investigate the 'pourability' of different liquids.

 Which liquids can be poured easily?

Children could devise a test in response to this question. They will need to consider:

◆ what equipment to use or make;
◆ what measurements they might take;
◆ how to make the comparison between different liquids a fair one.

AT 1 — MEASURING. PLANNING AND CARRYING OUT FAIR TESTS

One suggestion is shown here. Ask:

Q *Which liquid poured the best?*
What kinds of liquid pour easily?
Why do you think this is?
Can you make some liquids pour more easily?
How could you do this?
Is it always a good thing for liquids to pour easily?
Can you find out when it is better if the liquid is not runny?

d Solid or liquid?

Children could be shown and asked about mixtures of solids and liquids, and materials which will easily change from one to the other. Here are some examples.

Q *Is honey a solid or a liquid?*
Is an orange a solid or a liquid?
Is an egg a solid or a liquid?
What about when it is hard boiled?

pb

Materials provides further examples of 'liquids' and 'solids' that can be discussed.

AT 1   MEASURING

e Measuring solids and liquids

The following questions can be investigated practically with individual samples of a solid (such as a pebble) and a liquid (such as water with food colouring).

Q *How much space does it take up?*
How much does it weigh?

2 Gases

Experiences might be given of gases by making bubbles (which, of course, contain gas) by:

◆ using an (ozone friendly) aerosol can which dispenses a foam;
◆ blowing bubbles in soapy water;
◆ shaking a soft drink bottle (gently).

All these are gases bounded by liquids.

The fact that gases may be bounded by a solid can be shown by:

◆ blowing up a balloon;
◆ deflating and inflating a bicycle tyre.

OZONE-FRIENDLY AEROSOLS OFTEN HAVE A FLAMMABLE PROPELLANT

After such experiences children could be asked to say what gas they think is involved in each case.

Ask children to use their own observations and secondary source materials to find further examples of gases and to make a display showing different gases in action.

Examples might include helium and hot air balloons, oxygen in hospitals, breathing apparatus for firemen and divers, exhaust from cars and fumes from a chimney.

Materials gives examples of situations where gases are used.

Questions to prompt discussion and research in secondary sources might include:

  Are gases always colourless?
Are gases dangerous?
Do gases always smell?
Can water be made into a gas?
Is air a gas? Does it weigh anything? How do you think someone might try to weigh it?

Changing materials

AREAS FOR INVESTIGATION

◆ Tracing the origins of various materials.

◆ Investigating ways in which materials can be changed.

◆ Identifying the processes involved in the manufacture of different materials.

The emphasis here is on how materials can be changed. This theme complements and extends the previous two themes. The teachers' guide *Using energy* also considers ways in which some materials can be changed in the themes 'Hot and cold' and 'Fuels'.

KEY IDEAS

◆ Materials can be changed into different forms.

◆ Some materials can be changed permanently by heating, but in other materials the changes can be reversed by cooling.

◆ *Different forms of the same material have some different and some common properties.

◆ *Some materials occur naturally but may be purified or processed before use; others are made by chemically changing the raw materials.

(*Asterisks indicate ideas which will be developed morefully in later key stages.)

A LOOK AT
changing materials

Sources of materials are both non-living (the earth, sea, and air) and living (animals and plants).

Some materials may be used directly, but most need some processing. Wool, for example, is sheared, cleaned, perhaps dyed, spun, and woven or knitted. This processing does not change the essential composition of the material.

Other materials are made by changing raw materials into different materials. The raw material undergoes a permanent change and becomes a new material with quite different properties. Thus, brick is a manufactured material; its properties are quite different from those of the clay from which it was made. Crude oil and coal are naturally occurring materials which can be changed to produce thousands of different substances – such as plastics, dyes, artificial fibres, and medicines – which are very different from the original oil and coal.

While processing natural materials may not change their composition, it may alter their properties. Untreated cotton, cotton thread and a piece of woven cotton fabric behave differently when pulled. However, some properties of cotton, such as its solubility and the effect of heating it, are the same for all forms of cotton.

NATIONAL CURRICULUM PROGRAMME OF STUDY

Experiments on dissolving and evaporation should lead to developing ideas about solutions and solubility. [Pupils] should explore ways of separating and purifying mixtures such as muddy water, salty water and ink, by using evaporation, filtration and chromatography.

Pupils should explore the origins of a range of materials in order to appreciate that some occur naturally while many are made from raw materials. They should investigate the action of heat on everyday materials resulting in permanent change: these might include cooking activities and firing clay. Pupils should explore chemical changes in a number of everyday materials such as those that occur when mixing Plaster of Paris, mixing baking powder with vinegar, and when iron rusts. They should recognize that combustion of fuel releases energy and produces waste products including gases.

Finding out children's ideas

■ STARTER ACTIVITIES

1 Where do materials come from?

Start with a class discussion on the origin of a common object such as a wooden chair. Ask the children to suggest what it was like before it was a chair (pieces of wood), what it was like before that (a large single piece of wood), and before that (a tree). After the discussion, ask the children to do the same for a number of other objects such as:

◆ flour;
◆ a spoon;
◆ a piece of coloured fabric.

Q *What was it like before it was flour/a spoon/fabric? What was it like before that? And before that?*

Ask the children to record their ideas as a sequence of annotated drawings, as shown below. The number of drawings in any sequence is not fixed, and children should be encouraged to go back as far as they can.

material	what it was like before that	and before that	and before that	and before that	and before that
flour	wheat	seedlings	seeds		
piece of coloured cotton fabric	wasn't dyed – just a white colour	cotton thread	a kind of fluff which comes off a plant	plant without any fluff because it hasn't grown yet	seeds
spoon	piece of metal	thick liquid made out of metal	chemicals and liquids used to make metal liquid		

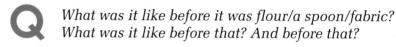

Discuss the drawings with the children to clarify what processes are being described. Questions could include:

Discuss the drawings with the children to clarify what processes are being described. Questions could include:

Q *Could you tell me what has happened to make the (object)? Where do these things take place? How long do you think it takes for all these things to happen?*

2 Natural or man-made?

Introduce a range of objects and materials and ask the children to group them under three headings:

◆ natural;
◆ man-made/synthetic;
◆ not sure.

Suitable safe examples would be natural wool, acrylic fibre, pieces of wood, metal, and plastic, cotton cloth, and salt.

Explore their reasons for their choice of category for the items.

Q *What makes you say these are natural/synthetic? Why have you put these in the 'not sure' group? What do you think 'natural'/'synthetic' means?*

3 Changing materials

The manufacture of objects and the production of new materials depend on the fact that materials can be changed in different ways. This activity focuses more closely on children's ideas about whether certain changes are possible, and how they may be brought about.

a What changes are possible?

The choice of items you show to children will depend on the particular changes you wish to consider. One such set might include a steel rod, a length of steel wire, iron filings, wire wool and foil.

! TAKE CARE WITH IRON FILINGS

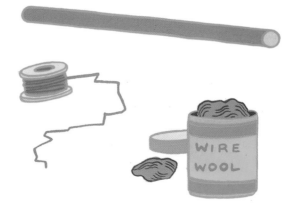

Children can be shown, for example, the steel rod and asked:

Do you think it is possible to change this into, for example, iron filings?
How might the change be made?
Why do you say this cannot be changed into, for example, foil?
Do you think it would be possible to change it into anything else that is not here?

b Changes with heating and cooling

Children could be shown various materials and asked to predict what they think would happen if they were heated. You might include solids such as steel, sugar and cotton wool; and liquids such as vinegar and treacle. Predictions could be written down as a table. In each case, children might also indicate whether and how the original material could be got back again.

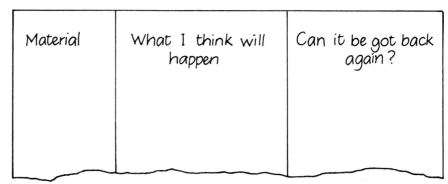

Material	What I think will happen	Can it be got back again?

If children mention that something might melt, you might raise the subject of mass conservation.

What can you say about the mass of the (steel) after it has melted?

This question introduces the idea that some attributes of the material change, while others remain the same.

Similarly, they might be asked to say what they think would happen if various materials were cooled down. Solids like steel could be mentioned but the emphasis should be on liquids such as water, vinegar or treacle.

4 Mixing and separating materials

When you feel it appropriate, explore children's ideas about the effects of mixing materials and ways of separating them. Children can be given different mixtures of materials or objects – for example, sand and sugar, pebbles and sand, steel and aluminium cans.

HEATING SHOULD ONLY BE DONE UNDER CLOSE ADULT SUPERVISION, IF AT ALL

Questions such as the following will help to reveal their ideas:

Q *Do you think this is all the same?*
What makes you think it is/is not?
How could you find out if you are right?

If a child states that there is more than one material, ask:

Q *Do you think they can be separated?*
How might you do it?
Do you think it could be done in any other way?

Children might also be given substances such as salt, plaster of Paris, and sand, and asked:

Q *What do you think would happen if these were mixed together?*
What do you think would happen if each of these was mixed with water? What makes you say that?

Children's ideas

Origins of materials

Many children tend to accept things as they are, and give the impression that objects have always existed in their current form. Some suggest that articles are obtained 'from a shop', and see no need to think beyond this point.

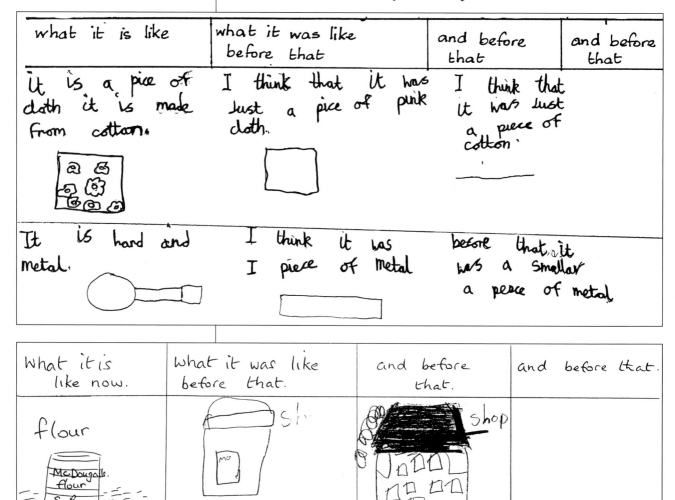

what it is like	what it was like before that	and before that	and before that
it is a pice of cloth it is made from cotton.	I think that it was Just a pice of pink cloth.	I think that it was Just a piece of cotton.	
It is hard and metal.	I think it was I piece of Metal	before that it was a Smaller a peace of metal	

What it is like now.	What it was like before that.	and before that.	and before that.
flour McDougalls. flour S.R.	sh MO	shop	

Some children say that some change or process has taken place, but refer only to the article being 'made in the factory'.

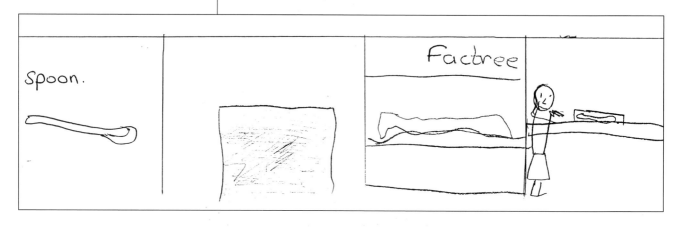

Spoon.   Factree

Older children may recognize and describe changes that are needed to produce an article from the original substance such as a plant or an ore.

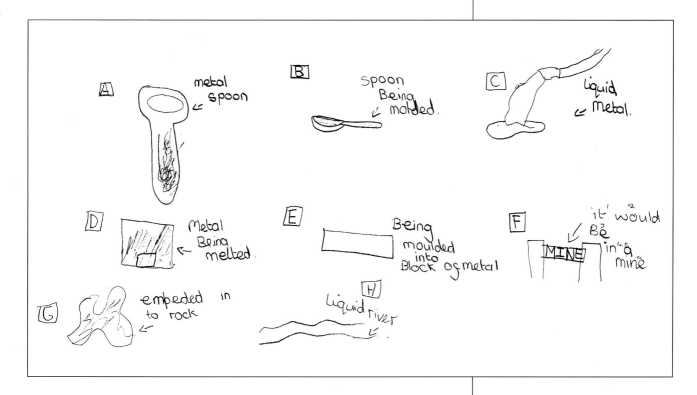

In some cases they may allude to the recycling of materials. In this case, ask questions to find whether they think this is the only source of the item.

An interesting distinction can be made between the idea that changes are needed for the production of new materials, and actual knowledge of the intermediate steps and the origin. For example, the origin of cotton is often given as 'from sheep'.

Activity 3 cloth			
what it is like	what it was like before that	and before that	and before that
It is very a cloth and very soft.	was It cotten on a weel.	It was on a mechean.	on a sheep

Changing materials

Children are likely to have experienced the melting of some materials, such as ice and chocolate. They readily use the word 'melt' in predicting what happens on heating. For substances with higher melting points, such as metals, they sometimes believe that the only effect of heating is to make them get hotter, or red hot. Those believing that metal melts may have differing ideas about the weight after melting.

It would melt. It would be a puddle of silver. The [metal] rod would be very heavy and the puddle would be very light because water doesn't weigh much.

When it's melted it wouldn't weigh anything at all. It is too soft.
It would weigh the same. Like a rock, if you dissolve a rock into lava it would weigh the same.

Even though most children indicate that water eventually boils when it is heated, they may not have the same idea for aqueous liquids such as vinegar.

It would get really hot and stay exactly the same.

In the teachers' guide *Using energy*, 'Hot and cold' (page 28) includes further ideas expressed by children about the changes of state brought about by heating and cooling (solid to liquid and liquid to gas).

Children are usually aware that some things burn. Here are some ideas about what happens to cotton wool when it is heated:

It would shrink and it would go hotter and go grey.

It would set on fire.

It will go black.

When asked if it is possible to change materials from one form into another children often show very slight appreciation of such possibilities. Some changes (such as from steel rod to filings) are considered more plausible than others (such as from steel rod to wire).

3.3

Helping children to develop their ideas

The chart opposite shows how you can help children to develop their ideas from starting points which have given rise to different ideas.

The centre rectangles contain starter questions.

The surrounding 'thought bubbles' contain the sorts of ideas expressed by children.

The further ring of rectangles contains questions posed by teachers in response to the ideas expressed by the children. These questions are meant to prompt children to think about their ideas.

The outer ovals indicate ways in which the children might respond to the teacher's questions.

Some of the shapes have been left blank, as a sign that other ideas may be encountered and other ways of helping children to develop their ideas may be tried.

1 Manufacturing materials and objects

Direct extension of the starter activity 'Where do materials come from?' (page 62) is an appropriate way of developing children's ideas.

Encourage children, either individually or in groups, to investigate the origins of various materials. They will need to use secondary sources such as books, magazines, videos and filmstrips; the activity is an excellent opportunity for children to learn to use these sources effectively to respond to specific questions, rather than just copying down the first thing they see.

More about materials considers the manufacture of different items. Some children may refer to the recycling of materials in manufacturing, and the same book can be used as part of a discussion about waste and recycling.

Support the work with secondary sources by:

◆ visits to factories and industrial museums;
◆ encouraging children to manufacture their own materials such as recycled paper, dyed wool or cotton, bricks, pottery, and bread.

The results of investigations can be summarized in the form of flow charts for display.

pb

! THIS NEEDS CAREFUL PLANNING AND AN ASSESSMENT OF WHAT HAZARDS MAY BE INVOLVED.
CHECK YOUR SCHOOL'S POLICY ON VISITS

AT 1   RECORDING

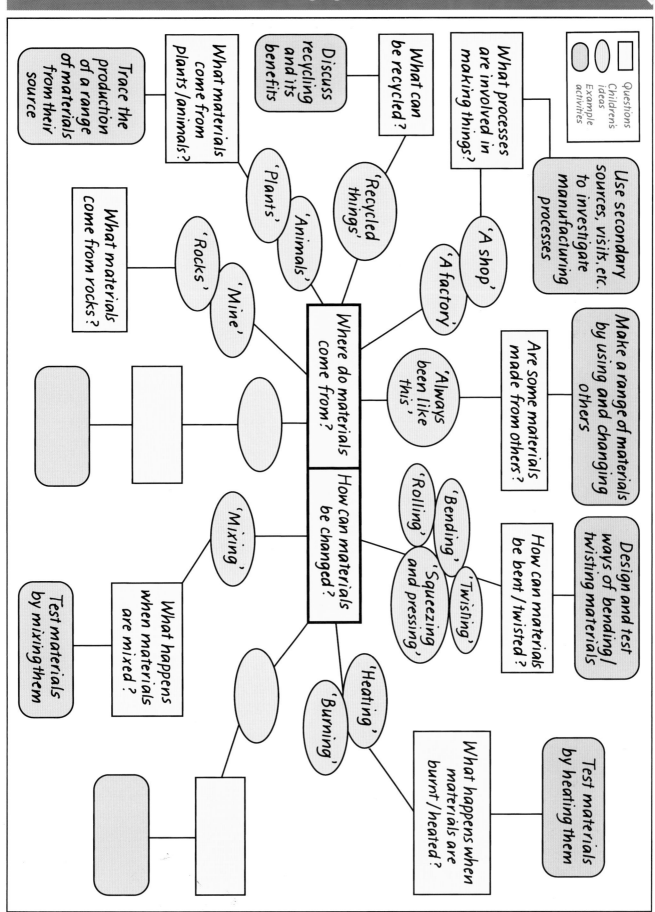

Key:
- Questions (rectangle)
- Children's ideas (small oval)
- Example activities (large oval)

Where do materials come from?

What processes are involved in making things?
- 'A shop'
- 'A factory'

Use secondary sources, visits, etc. to investigate manufacturing processes

What can be recycled?
- 'Recycled things'

Discuss recycling and its benefits

What materials come from plants/animals?
- 'Plants'
- 'Animals'

Trace the production of a range of materials from their source

What materials come from rocks?
- 'Rocks'
- 'Mine'

'Always been like this'

Are some materials made from others?

Make a range of materials by using and changing others

How can materials be changed?
- 'Bending'
- 'Rolling'
- 'Twisting'
- 'Squeezing and pressing'
- 'Mixing'
- 'Heating'
- 'Burning'

How can materials be bent/twisted?

Design and test ways of bending/twisting materials

What happens when materials are mixed?

Test materials by mixing them

What happens when materials are burnt/heated?

Test materials by heating them

2 Changing materials

Some changes to materials can be investigated more specifically, either in their own right or arising out of the above explorations. Examples might include the following.

a Pressing and rolling materials

Materials which can be pressed or rolled can be investigated, with and without tools. The effects of pressing or rolling materials such as Plasticine, pastry and Playdoh can be contrasted with those using elastic materials such as sponge.

b Heating and cooling substances

Activities related to some of the changes brought about by heating and cooling, such as melting, evaporating, boiling, freezing and condensation, are given in 'Hot and cold' in the teachers' guide *Using energy*.

Ask children to think about some of the predictions that they made during the starter activity (page 64) and gather further evidence. This will include:

◆ the use of secondary sources for some investigations, such as the effect of heating steel;

◆ practical tests on the heating of things such as a very small piece of cotton wool or a few drops of vinegar;

HEATING AND BURNING SHOULD BE DONE ONLY UNDER CLOSE ADULT SUPERVISION

HEATING SHOULD ONLY BE DONE UNDER CLOSE ADULT SUPERVISION

◆ classifying materials according to the effect heating has on them: those that melt, those that boil, those that change permanently;

◆ investigating the idea of weight conservation during melting – children could weigh a lump of ice before and after it melts.

AT 1   GENERAL

c Mixing and dissolving substances

Salt, sugar, sand, flour, clay, tea, instant coffee, hand washing powder and cooking oil are among the many things that can be added to water and the effects observed.

3.3

v

t   WHEN A SUBSTANCE HAS DISSOLVED COMPLETELY THE SOLUTION IS CLEAR

AT 1   GENERAL

e

!   CHECK CHILDREN'S PLANS FOR SAFETY BEFORE THEY START

!   CEMENT IS STRONGLY ALKALINE, AND CHILDREN USING IT MUST BE CLOSELY SUPERVISED BY AN ADULT. CHILDREN MUST WEAR EYE PROTECTION IF THEY HANDLE CEMENT POWDER. AVOID SKIN CONTACT WITH WET CEMENT

t   SALT DISSOLVES IN WATER WHILE CEMENT HARDENS. SAND MIXES WITH WATER BUT IS UNCHANGED

pb

AT 1   GENERAL

This can lead to much vocabulary work and the consideration of the term 'dissolving'. Ask:

Q *How can you tell whether something has dissolved or not?*
How can you find out how much of a substance will dissolve?
Can you get the substance back again once you have dissolved it?
What helps a substance to dissolve?
Do things dissolve only in water?

The first question requires experience of dissolving and non-dissolving events so that children can learn to distinguish between them. Children can then devise investigations to respond to the other questions.

Encourage the children to design and carry out fair tests. This will involve:

◆ consideration of what techniques are appropriate;

◆ deciding what measurements to take;

◆ selecting suitable equipment;

◆ identifying which variables to keep the same and which one to change;

◆ taking great care when heating things.

The effect of water on substances such as salt might then be compared with that of water on, for example, sand, plaster of Paris and cement. Discussions could consider the following questions:

Q *What changes can be seen when water is mixed with salt/cement?*
Can the salt/cement and water be separated again?
What do you think the water is doing when it is mixed with salt/cement?

Materials and *More about materials* give other examples of mixing things with different results. These may form the basis of discussions and some further investigation.

d Separating materials

Children can investigate ways of separating materials that have been mixed. Set them simple problems, separating things such as:

◆ sand and salt, which can be done by adding water to dissolve the salt and relates directly to the extraction of salt from the ground;

- sand and iron filings, which can be separated with a magnet;
- mud or similar substance in water, which can be separated by filtering.

Children could check that the salt was dissolved in the water by allowing a saucer of the solution to dry up. Those who suggest that the salt was in the water all along could put out a second saucer of the water before it was added to the sand and salt mixture.

Encourage the children to relate these techniques to processes that are used in different industries, which they can find out about from secondary sources.

Some children may observe that materials change 'naturally' or that it is possible to slow down changes in materials by preserving them. *Materials* gives examples which may be discussed.

CHAPTER 4

Assessment

4.1 Introduction

You will already have assessed your children's ideas and skills by using this teachers' guide. The starter activities in each theme will have enabled you to discover their existing ideas and skills; and you will have been able to gather information about the children's progress during and after the activities designed to develop their ideas.

This chapter is designed to help you to express this information about your pupils' achievements in terms of the National Curriculum levels. It does this by looking at examples of children's work and seeing how they link to the general statements of the curriculum.

By pointing out features of the examples which indicate activity at a certain level we hope to show you what to look for in your pupils' work as evidence of achievement at one level or another. The features we look at are those which typify a particular level – which make it a level 3 rather than level 2 or 4 achievement, for instance – rather than those which match to specific statements of attainment. This helps in assessing work even when there is no statement of attainment relating to a particular concept at that level.

It should be possible to use the work which your pupils have already done in order to assess their achievement in relation to this part of the curriculum. It should not be necessary to give special exercises in order to complete what is required for teachers' assessment of this part of pupils' work.

There are two sets of examples provided. The first is concerned with the assessment of skills in the context of the activities related to the concepts covered in this guide. The second deals with the development of these concepts.

4.2 Assessment of skills (AT1)

The teacher planned that groups of children would explore the properties of a selection of both natural and manufactured everyday materials. One group of children were presented with chocolate, detergent, flour, sugar, oats, butter and water, which were within the children's experience. A further group handled a different selection of materials which included silk, wool, cotton and acrylic. Another group explored different metals. Following discussion of the properties of the materials, the children were encouraged to test their ideas.

Children in one group predicted that powders would dissolve in water.

During discussion they decided that some powders would dissolve in hot water but not in cold. They selected a number of powders and proceeded to test their ideas.

A further group of children had noticed that materials had different strengths. They planned a test which would enable them to decide which was the strongest and weakest fibre.

Children who had looked at metals developed an investigation to test the strength of different metals.

Ask questions, predict and hypothesize

Amy and her group

These responses to the materials the children were handling demonstrate that they were using their everyday experiences to generate testable hypotheses. Amy and her group have noticed that when detergent is mixed with water it makes bubbles, and that detergent removes grease from plates.

> **Aroe Chocolate Bar**
> It has bubbles inside it, on the otside you can see different coloured circles from the bubbles. On the Bottom there are holes. When looking through a mangnifi glass you can see the bubbles in great detail. It is made with milk chocolate.
>
> **Washing up liquid**
> A Green coloured soapy liquid. When mixed with water it makes bubbles, and it clears grease off plates. Tiny bubbles float underneath the water as well. Smells of Soap and is quite thick.

> **Experiment**
> **Bending Metal**
> We are finding out how strong some matals are
>
> **What we did**
> We did the experiment with some different metals which are silver Nickle, allininium, zink, brass, mild steel, stainless steel,
> We bent them with a pair of plyers untill they snapped and here are the results.
>
> **Results**
>
> | Nickle | 0 too hard to snap |
> |---|---|
> | allininium | 29 and snapped |
> | zinc | 13 and snapped |
> | Brass | 57 and snapped |
> | Mild steel | 60 and snapped |
> | steel | 56 and snapped |
>
> **Why we think this happened**
> We found out that mild steel was the strongest, and the easiest to snap was zink, zinc, next was aluminium. We couldn't snap the Nickle because it was too small (a disc)

Matthew and his group

Ben

Some children (such as Matthew) had expressed the view that metals were strong, and the teacher encouraged them to develop their ideas into an investigation. Testable ideas of this nature indicate achievement of level 3.

Material	Did Dissolve	Didn't Dissolve	Not Sure
Sugar	✓ in cold water	✗	✗
Alum	✗	fig 3 not in hot or cold	✗
Epsum salt	✗	✗	✓ were not certain
table salt	✗	✓ in hot or cold water	✗
talc	✗	✓ in hot or cold	✗
flour	✗	✓ in hot or cold water	✗

We tried to dissolve all these powders by mixing them with cold and hot water (these were our results)

Ben's prediction that powders will dissolve in hot water seems to be based on different everyday experiences of some powders dissolving which he has linked together. This is another testable idea which indicates achievement of level 3.

Observe, measure, and manipulate variables

Although Ben has recognized that all the powders should be mixed with both hot and cold water, he has not yet appreciated that the quantities of powders and liquids should be carefully measured. However, he is making a series of observations as required of work at level 2.

Emma

We pulled out one fibre from each piece of material. We stuck it to the table with Sellotape Then we tied a loop on the bottom of the fibre and then we put an S-hook through the loop. Then we got some string tied it to a tub. Then we put a small number of weights in the tub and kept adding until the fibre broke we used the same tub each time to make the experiment fair we wrote down the breaking weight.

Name of fabric	Weight Breaking in g
linen	1035g
wool	7g
silk	180g
cotton	16g
nylon	48g
Acrylic	241g

What we found out

We found out that linen was the most strongest fabric and wool was the weakest fabric. It might of been different if they was the same thickness and size they mite of been different.

Matthew's investigation of the strength of different metals shows that the group made some attempt to quantify their observations. They had carefully counted the number of times each metal bent until it snapped. These attempts at quantified observations are at level 3, although they did not control the shape and size of the pieces.

Emma describes her attempts to design a fair test of the strength of different fibres. She explains that the same tub was used each time, and that weights were added so that the point at which each thread snapped could be carefully measured. The work of pupils who recognize the importance of developing a fair test is at level 4.

Interpret results and evaluate scientific evidence

Emma points out some of the limitations of her investigation. She mentions that the thickness of the fibre was not controlled and that this could have affected the reliability of her results. Emma's interpretation of her findings, together with her appreciation that her conclusions may not be reliable, meets the criteria for level 3. The further conclusions she draws suggest that this aspect of her work is reaching level 4.

4.3 Assessment of children's understanding (part of AT3)

Level 2

Pupils who have reached level 2 should recognize some of the ways in which materials differ, and be able to group materials together on the basis of observable features.

This piece of work demonstrates the pupil's ability to group different materials. Paul's collection of different items has been sorted into groups such as metals, wood, and plastic. This grouping strategy suggests that Paul decided at the outset to put items together according to the material used in their manufacture. Groupings based on observable features indicate achievement of level 2.

Gemma mentions that rubber, aluminium and leather are all flexible. Records of this kind, which show that different materials can share the same property, are at level 2 and indicate that an understanding of how properties relate to their uses, necessary for level 3, is being developed.

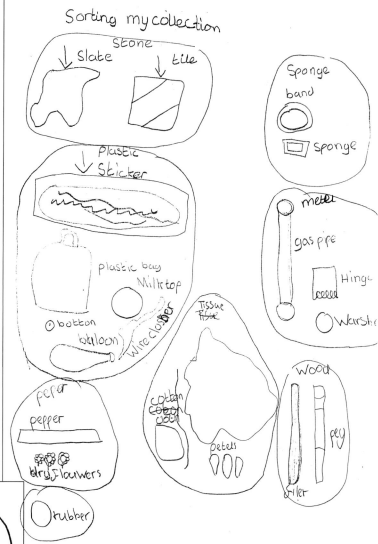

Paul

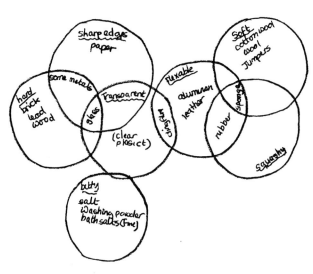

Gemma

Level 3

At this level, pupils are aware of how the ways in which materials are used can be related to their properties. Work which demonstrates an understanding of the origins of some materials indicates achievement of level 3.

> Plastic Container-
>
> Plastic containers can come in different shapes and sizes you can keep anything in them anything at all. You can have them different colours aswell.

Louise

Louise has described a number of ways in which plastic is used. Further questioning would clarify whether she is able to relate these uses to the properties of plastic. This work is approaching level 3. In order to reach this level, children would have to exhibit an understanding of the relationship between the properties of materials and the ways in which they are used.

> Materials
>
> Now Tyre.
>
> Rubber tyre.
> A rubber tyre is a security thing that secures a intube so it doesn't pop. It is rough and thick.
>
> Before
>
> This is a peice of (Plastic)(w) rubber, which is smooth and can be any colour
>
> Before that
>
> Dead Animals
> Here is a Dead Animal which has been shot for rubber.
>
> Before that.
>
> Animal
> Here is the animal living happily in peace untill he gets caught, to be used for rubber

Pat

Within a topic on bicycles, Pat mentions some of the properties of the rubber tyre. She is aware that the tyre is thick and rough; however, she does not mention the flexibility of rubber or that it can be shaped. Pat includes in her description her belief that rubber comes from animals, indicating that she needs more opportunity to consider the origins of different materials. Since Pat does not relate clearly the properties of rubber to the way it is used as a tyre, and is unaware of the origins of rubber, her work has not yet reached level 3.

Adam demonstrates an understanding of the relationship between the properties of wood and the different ways in which wood is used. He points out that wood can be carved and is a popular material. This understanding of the link between the properties of materials and the way they are used meet the criteria of level 3.

Adam

MATERIAL	USE	REASONS
Wood	cupboard tree door shelf, table box Paintbrush chair windowframes, fence gate	It is easy to carve and it is popular

Level 4

Children at this level have a general awareness of some of the properties of the solids, liquids and gases which they encounter in their everyday experience. They should be able to use this understanding to classify materials as solids, liquids, and gases.

Hannah

Solids

Solids are things that do not run or like liquids and are things that you can feel like a pencil or, a peice of wood. meatal or paper and many more.

— a pencil

liquids

Liquids are things that run and like solids you can feel and they feel wet. Some liquids are vinegar, water, washing up liquid, paint and many more. Liquids need to be kept in containors otherwise they spill and or spread out on the floor

— liquid cept in containor

— liquid out of containor

Gases

Unlike liquids and solids you can not feel gases and if you put it in water the gases will rise in eg:
Little bubles eg

— Bubbles rising from water

Hannah has recognized some of the properties of solids, liquids and gases. In addition to this, she has made an attempt to classify materials based on her understanding of their properties. The teacher might challenge Hannah's understanding of solids and liquids by asking her to classify flour or salt. She could also be encouraged to generate more examples of gases. Work which demonstrates an ability to classify objects as solids, liquids, and gases satisfies the criteria of level 4.

Level 5

At this level, pupils should use different techniques for separating and purifying mixtures.

Catherine's work demonstrates her attempts to explore the component parts of a soil sample. She observed and felt the soil, and later separated the soil using water. Catherine describes how separating the soil using water enabled her to identify components of the soil. Although this work shows an ability to use one separation technique, part of the criterion for level 5, further evidence of an ability to separate and purify other substances would be necessary to confirm that her ideas had reached level 5.

Catherine

The soil is dry and lumpy and not very smooth it has dead things and twigs in it.
It is a brown-black odour.

In the soil we found a staple a bit of rubber and stones.

We have four layers in our wet soil.

Top layer contains bits of twigs and rubbish the second layer contains dirty water the Third layer rubbish and Bits of twigs. The Fourth layer contains soil.

Top and third ~~and~~ ~~~~ and Second layer are inorganic.

The fourth layer is made up of inorganic and organic materials.

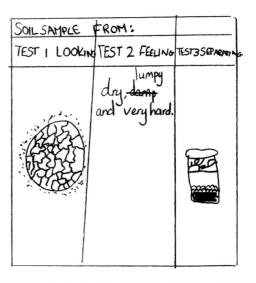

SOIL SAMPLE FROM:

TEST 1 LOOKING | TEST 2 FEELING | TEST 3 SEPARATING

dry, ~~damp~~ lumpy and very hard.

CHAPTER 5

Background science

What are materials?

The word 'material' can sometimes suggest nothing more than textile fabrics. Its wider sense, however, includes every substance that things are made from, including metals, ceramics, plastics, rubber, wood, glass, cement, leather, bone, textiles, glues, paints, dyes, solvents, foodstuffs, medicines – in short, any substance of a particular chemical composition, however simple or complex that might be.

From a look around any room, the influence of choice between materials in our lives is apparent. The balance between traditional and modern materials varies according to individual taste: a clay plant pot or a plastic one, a woollen pullover or an acrylic one. Looking outside at the built environment, we might, for example, see pavements of cobbles, flagstones, manufactured paving slabs or tarmac – different materials serving the same purpose.

Describing and comparing materials

It is important to know how particular materials behave. Rubber, for example, is a flexible material and so bridges are not made out of it; but tyres, which need to flex, are. The way a material responds to a particular treatment such as stretching or squashing is a property of that material.

Some properties are simply features of the material and can be observed directly by sight or touch. Examples include **shape**, **colour** and **texture**. That is not to say that children will always find these features straightforward to understand. Young children, for instance, often confuse smoothness (to do with the texture or 'feel' of a surface) with softness (to do with the feel experienced when pressing into a material).

Transparency is another directly observable property. A transparent material lets the light through so that what is on the other side of it can be seen clearly. A translucent material also lets light through, but in a diffuse way so that you cannot clearly see something on the other side of it. Frosted glass has been shaped to make it **translucent**, whereas ordinary smooth window glass is transparent. Materials which do not transmit light at all are called **opaque**.

The properties of **weight**, **mass** and **volume** can be estimated and measured.

◆ Mass is a measure of the reluctance of an object to move; the more massive it is the harder it is to move. It can be measured with a beam balance.

◆ Weight is the force exerted on an object by gravity. It can be measured with a spring balance.

When an object is on Earth and at rest, it will produce the same reading on both kinds of balance. But on the Moon, where gravity is one-sixth that of the Earth, the weight will be one-sixth of its Earth value, although the mass will remain the same here or anywhere else. Mass is a more fundamental property than weight because the inertia of an object does not vary from one place to another. Since we do not normally distinguish between weight and mass in everyday speech, we talk of weighing on a balance and not 'massing' (finding the mass).

◆ Volume is the amount of space that an object takes up.

Volume is normally used in the purchase of liquids (pints of milk and litres of petrol) and can be measured with a calibrated jug or other container. Solids also have a volume. If the solid has a regular shape, its volume can be calculated from its dimensions. If not, it can be placed in some water in a measuring jug to see how much the water level rises.

While mass and volume are properties of an object, the ratio of mass to volume is characteristic of the material. Thus different amounts of copper wire might be bought, but for all those amounts the ratio of mass to volume will be the same. The ratio is converted into a simple figure by dividing the mass of an object in grams by its volume in cubic centimetres. The result is known as the **density** of the material. 1 cm³ of water has a mass of 1 gram, so the density of water is 1. The density of copper is 8.95, so 1 cm³ has a mass of 8.95 grams. This situation is made more complicated by the fact that many 'materials' vary in composition, and may therefore vary in density. For example, skimmed milk is slightly denser than full cream milk since it contains less fat, which is less dense than water. Polythene is a plastic which is made in high and low density forms. Carrier bags may be made of either type; the low density kind is softer and more flexible, while the high density kind is crinkly and rustles when the bag is crumpled.

Materials can be treated to change their properties; for instance, they can be heated or bent. Where such a change leaves the material as the same substance, however altered it is, the characteristic that has been changed is called a **physical** property of the material. Examples are strength and hardness. Similarly, the previously mentioned properties of shape, colour, texture, transparency, 'weight' and volume are all physical properties.

Properties	Contrasting adjectives	Measuring
Strength	strong – weak	amount of force needed to break it (generally by stretching or squashing)
Toughness	tough – brittle	resistance to development of cracks
Stiffness	stiff – stretchy/ bendy/compressible	how stiff, flexible, bendy, floppy it is
Hardness	hard – soft	whether it is firm or yields to pressure – resistance to being cut or scratched

The table on the left outlines the differences between **strength, toughness, stiffness** and **hardness** which, although they are different attributes, may sometimes be used interchangeably in everyday speech.

Confusing these properties can have unfortunate consequences. It was once recommended that diamonds should be identified by striking them with a hammer. Although diamonds are the hardest known substance and will scratch and cut anything else, they are also quite brittle and will shatter if struck! Hardness is not the same as toughness.

Toughness and strength can also be contrasted. Polythene is tough: it does not break when dropped. However, it is does not have much **tensile strength** (resistance to **tension**; that is, pulling). It is easy to tear apart. In contrast, glass is brittle, yet relatively strong in tension (see the table of tensile strengths on the next page).

The following examples illustrate the difference between stiffness and strength. A piece of chalk is stiff but weak, while steel is both stiff and strong. Jelly is flexible and weak while nylon is both flexible and strong.

Consideration of the meanings of these properties leads to some possible ways of comparing materials in respect of them.

Examples of ways of comparing strength, hardness, toughness and stiffness

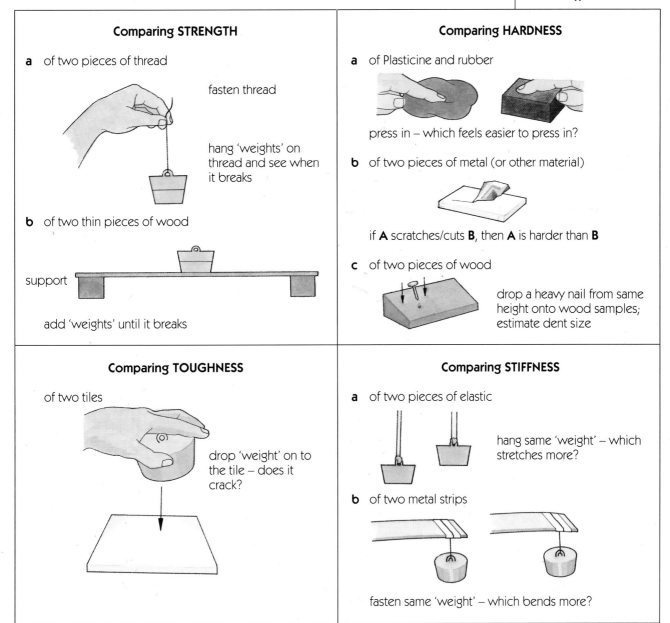

Comparing STRENGTH

a   of two pieces of thread

fasten thread

hang 'weights' on thread and see when it breaks

b   of two thin pieces of wood

support

add 'weights' until it breaks

Comparing HARDNESS

a   of Plasticine and rubber

press in – which feels easier to press in?

b   of two pieces of metal (or other material)

if **A** scratches/cuts **B**, then **A** is harder than **B**

c   of two pieces of wood

drop a heavy nail from same height onto wood samples; estimate dent size

Comparing TOUGHNESS

of two tiles

drop 'weight' on to the tile – does it crack?

Comparing STIFFNESS

a   of two pieces of elastic

hang same 'weight' – which stretches more?

b   of two metal strips

fasten same 'weight' – which bends more?

In thinking about the above comparisons, a clear distinction must be made between comparing objects and comparing materials. Everything done to two samples should be the same, so that one object is fairly tested against another. To make it a fair test of the materials, however, the dimensions of each sample should be taken into account. (This does not apply to hardness.) Suppose, for example, a piece of cotton and a piece of silk are pulled until they break. The 'weight' – that is, force – needed to do this gives an indication as to which thread is actually stronger. It does not show whether cotton is a stronger material than silk unless allowance is made for the thickness of each of the threads. One way of doing this is by having threads of equal thickness, but that is not always easy to achieve. Instead, the thickness of the threads should be measured in millimetres. These figures should then be squared to give the area in square millimetres. The force needed to break each thread should be measured in newtons. Dividing this figure by the area gives the tensile strength of the material in newtons per square millimetre (N/mm^2).

Here are some typical values.

Material	tensile strength (in millions N per m²)
high tensile engineering steel	400 – 1000
wrought iron	140 – 280
glass	30 – 170
ordinary brick	5
cotton	350
spider's thread	240
wood (spruce)	along grain: 100
	across grain: 3

Materials are used in **compression** as well as in tension. A suspension bridge is a tension structure, since the load pulls on the suspension cables. A stone arch bridge is a compression structure, with the load pressing on the stonework. The effect of compression varies with the material and its shape. A soft material such as Plasticine will spread out sideways. A brittle material like stone will retain its shape until it is overloaded, and then crumble or explode into pieces. A long, slim sample may buckle and a shell structure like a tin can may crumple. Owing to this variation, it is often only possible to estimate **compressive strength**. Materials such as cement and cast iron are much stronger in compression than in tension – they pull apart much more easily than they collapse when pressed together.

The word **elastic** can refer both to a kind of material and to a property. An elastic material is one which can be deformed by stretching, compressing, bending or twisting, and will return to its original shape when released. The most familiar example is rubber (which in some uses is actually called 'elastic'). Many other materials, even relatively stiff ones such as steel, have elastic properties; steel is used to make springs. **Plastic** behaviour is shown by Plasticine and putty. When they are distorted, they remain in their new shape rather than going back to what they were like before. Plastics are not usually 'plastic' in this sense, although they were at some stage in their manufacture when they could be moulded and shaped. Plastic behaviour can also be found in metals: under sufficient stress they flow like liquids.

Liquids flow to different degrees. Those which flow easily are said to be **mobile**, while those that do not are called **viscous**. The most viscous liquids, such as pitch, tar and toffee, are hard to tell from solids. The viscosity of a liquid can be judged by observing how easily it pours.

Another important property of liquids is their function as **solvents**; that is, they can dissolve other substances. Taking any one liquid, some substances will be found to dissolve in it while others do not. Strictly speaking, however, solubility is not an 'either–or' matter. It is a measurable quantity expressed in grams of a substance (solute) that can be dissolved in 100 grams of liquid. To say that some substances dissolve better in water than others means that more will dissolve in the same quantity of water. A substance may dissolve in one liquid but not in another. For example, a smear of oil-based paint may not come off with water but will dissolve in turpentine. Salt dissolves in water but not in petrol.

When something dissolves it mixes perfectly with the solvent and the resulting solution should be transparent – though it may be coloured. This is often not the case for things which commonly are said to dissolve – instant coffee, for example. Here, in fact, small solid particles remain in **suspension** in the liquid, making it murky. In such cases it is probably best to focus on the 'disappearance' of the solid granules as evidence of dissolving.

Some everyday instances of dissolving are difficult to recognize – is anything dissolving when a pot of tea is brewed or when dye runs in the wash? Moreover, everyday use tends to restrict the use of the word to solids intermingling with liquids, while in fact liquids will also dissolve in liquids, – for example, oil in petrol – and gases in liquids – as in fizzy drinks. There are even 'solid solutions' of one solid in another, as in certain metal alloys where two metals were mixed when molten and have remained equally well mixed while solidifying.

Solubility can be a useful factor in deciding how to separate solids and liquids. In real (as opposed to instant) coffee the grounds can be separated from the soluble substances by **filtration** through paper. A filter would not remove the dissolved salt from salty water. In this case the solution can be heated to drive off the water by boiling, or it can be left to **evaporate** slowly, to leave the salt behind. Pure water can be recovered from a boiling salt solution by catching the steam and cooling it to condense it back into a liquid. This is the process of **distillation**, which is also used to make alcoholic spirits such as whisky by separating alcohol from a relatively watery fermented brew.

Filtration, evaporation and distillation are all commonly used to separate substances. A further method can be used to separate liquids that do not mix, such as oil and water. If they are poured into a vessel, then left to **settle**, the oil will separate completely from the water and float on it. If the vessel has a tap at the bottom, opening the tap will let out the water.

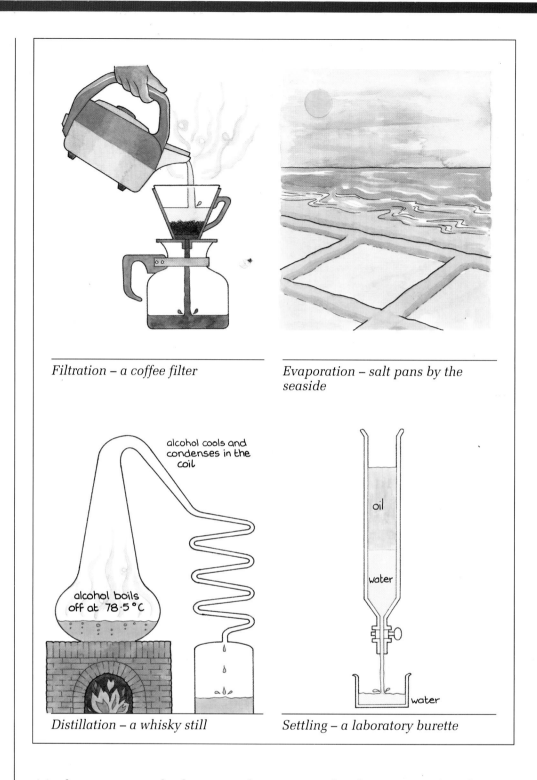

Filtration – a coffee filter

Evaporation – salt pans by the seaside

alcohol cools and condenses in the coil

alcohol boils off at 78·5 °C

oil

water

water

Distillation – a whisky still

Settling – a laboratory burette

Another property of substances that may need to be measured is their **acidity** or **alkalinity**. This is measured on the **pH** scale, which runs from 1 for strongly acid through 7 for neutral to 14 for strongly alkaline. For example, some soils, such as those containing a lot of peat, are acidic and certain plants like heathers and rhododendrons grow well in them while others do not. Similarly other soils are alkaline, as in chalky areas. Clematis and viburnum thrive in alkaline soil. Most plants prefer a slightly acid to neutral soil. A soil testing kit contains a chemical indicator; this may be a liquid, or paper impregnated with liquid. Water is added to the soil and it is shaken to dissolve soluble components. The indicator shows the pH of the soil by turning a particular colour, which is compared with a chart. An indicator is often a plant extract:

you can improvise one by briefly boiling red cabbage in a little water. The resulting solution turns red in acid conditions, blue in alkaline. Hydrangeas, interestingly, are self-indicating by bearing blue flowers in acid soil and pink ones in alkaline soil.

Acids are often regarded as dangerous. Some acids, if not diluted, can burn the skin – for example, the sulphuric acid in a car battery. Most commonly encountered acids are weak enough or dilute enough to be harmless, such as the citric acid in oranges and the acetic acid in vinegar. Some alkalis, such as the caustic soda used for cleaning, can be more corrosive than strong acids and should be treated with great care. Others, such as bicarbonate of soda, are harmless.

Origin, manufacture and uses of materials

Materials can be found in and among the rocks of the Earth, in the oceans, in the atmosphere and in plants and animals. Gold is found as lumps of pure metal in the ground; common salt is found in the sea; the oxygen used in hospitals is found in the air; natural dyes are found in plants; wool is found on sheep. For all these naturally occurring materials some processing is needed before the material can be used. This processing may involve purifying the material by removing unwanted substances from it. The separation processes referred to earlier may be used – air can be cooled to liquefy it then distilled at a very low temperature to separate oxygen from the other gases; evaporation of sea water produces salt. Other manufacturing processes may be involved to get the material into the shape and form required – the gold shaped to form a ring, the wool spun, dyed and woven to make a garment. Both separation and manufacturing processes are physical changes, because the chemical composition of the material does not change. Common salt is still sodium chloride whether it is in the sea or in a salt cellar.

Many materials have to be made from a naturally occurring raw material. One substance is chemically changed into another. Crude oil is a raw material from which many thousands of materials – plastics, dyes, artificial fibres, medicines and so on – are made. It is itself a complex mixture of substances which have first to be separated from one another by distillation.

The raw material from which plaster of Paris is made is a rock called gypsum. When heated, it changes chemically to become a fine white powder. When water is added it turns back into a solid substance similar to the original rock. Here the water has quite a different effect from that of a solvent. It combines with the powder to change it into another material. The change can be reversed by heating the solidified plaster, but that is not the case with some other materials. For example, cement is made by heating limestone and clay, and is made to solidify by adding water (it will actually harden under water). Once the cement has set, heating it will not restore the original limestone and clay. Heating clay by itself to make pottery also produces irreversible changes.

In all these chemical changes it is quite clear that the new substance has different properties from the original one. Cement is a soft powder which turns into a solid mass when water is added. Thus manufacturing often involves a change which brings about a new set of desired characteristics. Even physical treatments which change only the shape and form of a material can result in a radical change of properties. Thin glass fibres are much stronger, weight for weight, than solid glass. A metal bar may be flattened into a sheet or drawn out into a wire, or even ground into a powder. The bar, sheet, wire and powder are all of the same metal, yet each will behave differently because of the differences in form. Nevertheless they will share some characteristics, such as melting point and solubility, because they are still the same material.

The properties of a material help determine its use. Windows are made out of glass because it is transparent; petrol can be used to take tar off cars because tar dissolves in it; sandpaper is used for smoothing wood because the sand is rough and hard; rubber is used for balloons because it stretches.

Sometimes the properties of materials may be combined to produce a material which has properties which neither alone can provide. Copper is a soft metal; zinc is rather brittle. Together they make the alloy brass, which is hard and tough. There are also composite materials, such as glass reinforced plastic (GRP, 'Fibreglass'), which is made from fine glass fibres set in tough plastic. It combines the tensile strength of the glass with the toughness of the plastic.

The properties of a material are not the only factor to influence its use. Gold is a relatively soft metal, easily scratched. Nevertheless it is still used for jewellery for aesthetic reasons – it is shiny and does not tarnish – and because it is scarce and therefore valuable. Aesthetic and economic considerations may also influence the choice between materials which have the same uses. Wood, steel and plastic are all strong enough to make chairs; they can all be manufactured in various ways into suitable shapes. Which one is chosen may depend on appearance, comfort or cost, or all of these. The toughness and hardness of the materials may also influence the chair's durability, which again bears on its suitability for a particular purpose; a chair in a public hall needs to be much more durable than one in a dining room.

Solids, liquids and gases

The word 'solid' can convey a number of different meanings, particularly when used as an adjective. A solid ball is one that is not hollow, whereas a solid table is a firm and rigid one. 'Solid' also refers to three-dimensional bodies in mathematics. Children are probably less likely to have heard of the fewer alternative meanings of 'liquid', such as its use to describe a bird's song. (And 'gas' has various slang meanings.) When the three words 'solid', 'liquid' and 'gas' are used together it is in the sense of three states (or **phases**) of a substance.

Possibly each word conjures up an image of a specific example – a solid steel bar, liquid water, and gas in a cooker. But solids can be extremely varied. They include soft materials such as Plasticine and cotton wool, and powders like flour and sand. Liquids do not have to flow as easily as water; they may be viscous, like treacle. Gases are not all light and invisible: chlorine is green, and xenon is so heavy that a balloon filled with it slams into the floor and bursts. This leads to a consideration of what are the defining characteristics of each of the three states.

A solid has a definite shape. It remains that same shape unless a force acts upon it. Thus cotton wool is a solid; despite the fact that its shape can be so easily changed, it does have a definite shape. Powders are also solids because even though the whole mass does not have a definite shape, each little bit does, whether it is a regular crystal as in sand or sugar, or amorphous (literally having no particular shape) like a grain of flour.

A liquid has no fixed shape, but it keeps the same volume when it is poured into a different container. Even the thickest liquids will settle into the shape of the container eventually.

A gas has no fixed shape or volume. It will thus always spread out to fill the whole of the space in which it is contained. Even the lightest gases have a certain 'weight'. Most gases are colourless, and it is probably this invisibility which can give the impression that they are insubstantial. Gases are 'revealed' as bubbles in a liquid or in a foam. Smoke is not a gas, but fine specks of solid suspended in the air.

These characteristics make it sound as if the distinctions are clear cut. However, there are borderline cases of substances that may appear to behave like solids in some respects and liquids in others. Even solid rock, for example, flows when subjected to great heat and pressure, as happens deep inside the Earth.

We are used to seeing particular materials in particular states – steel as a solid, water as a liquid and air as a gas. This is because we usually experience the materials at particular temperatures – the narrow temperature range in which we can live. The only really familiar changes of state are those of water, which has a very small distance between its freezing and boiling points. Ice and steam are easily produced. In fact water can exist as a gas below its boiling point, when it evaporates into the air to become water vapour. Air can hold only a certain amount of water vapour; the warmer it is, the more vapour it can hold, which is why when the temperature falls in the evening dew drops out of the air on to the ground. In contrast, steam above boiling point can exist on its own as a pure gas. (What is thought of as 'steam' – the visible cloud coming from a kettle – is not actually steam, which is invisible. There is a small transparent region of real steam next to the spout. But as it emerges into the cool air it condenses into suspended droplets of liquid water, which form the cloud you can see.)

Changes of state are reversible. The changes and the associated words are shown in the diagram on the next page.

Water vapour can be seen to condense on a cold day. When you breathe out on to a cold window, water vapour in your breath condenses into droplets of liquid water (often referred to as 'condensation').

Similarly, steel can change state and can be melted at a high enough temperature. Air can be cooled to form a liquid. The temperature at which a solid changes to a liquid (**melting point**) or a liquid to a true gas, as opposed to a vapour (**boiling point**) are characteristic of the substance concerned.

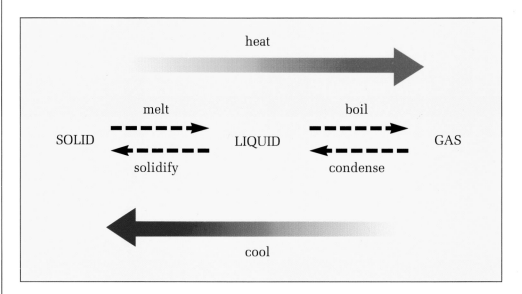

Heating does not always bring about the reversible changes indicated in the diagram above. As mentioned previously, it sometimes causes permanent change, as when clay is fired or a cake is baked. Heating also often results in a material burning; that is, it combines rapidly with oxygen from the air in a chemical reaction which gives out heat. That is, a flame appears as the material is split up and combined with oxygen from the air. Solids (such as wood), liquids (such as petrol) and gases (such as natural gas – methane) can all burn.

Index

Trial schools

The SPACE Project and the Trust are grateful to the governors, staff, and pupils of all the trial schools. It will be obvious to readers of these guides how much we are indebted to them for their help, and especially for the children's drawn and written records of their hard work and their growing understanding of science.

All Saints Primary School, Barnet, Hertfordshire
Ansdell County Primary School, Lytham St Anne's, Lancashire
Bishop Endowed Church of England Junior School, Blackpool
Brindle Gregson Lane Primary School, Lancashire
Brookside Junior and Infants School, Knowsley
Chalgrove JMI School, Finchley, London N3
Christ the King Roman Catholic Primary School, Blackpool
English Martyrs Roman Catholic Primary School, Knowsley
Fairlie County Primary School, Skelmersdale, Lancashire
Fairway JMI School, Mill Hill, London NW7
Foulds Primary School, Barnet, Hertfordshire
Frenchwood County Primary School, Preston
Grange Park Primary School, London N21
Hallesville Primary School, Newham, London E6
Heathmore Primary School, Roehampton, London SW15
Honeywell Junior School, London SW11
Huyton Church of England Junior School, Knowsley
Longton Junior School, Preston
Mawdesley Church of England Primary School, Lancashire
Moor Park Infants School, Blackpool
Mosscroft County Primary School, Knowsley
Nightingale Primary School, London E18
Oakhill Primary School, Woodford Green, Essex
Park Brow County Primary School, Knowsley
Park View Junior School, Knowsley
Purford Green Junior School, Harlow, Essex
Ronald Ross Primary School, London SW19
Rosh Pinah School, Edgeware, Middlesex
Sacred Heart Junior School, Battersea, London SW11
St Aloysius Roman Catholic Infants School, Knowlsey
St Andrew's Roman Catholic Primary School, Knowsley
St Bernadette's Roman Catholic Primary School, Blackpool
St James's Church of England Junior School, Forest Gate, London E7
St John Fisher Roman Catholic Primary School, Knowsley
St John Vianney Roman Catholic Primary School, Blackpool
St Mary and St Benedict Roman Catholic Primary School, Bamber Bridge, Preston
St Peter and St Paul Roman Catholic Primary School, Knowsley
St Theresa's Roman Catholic Primary School, Blackpool
St Theresa's Roman Catholic Primary School, Finchley, London N3
Scarisbrick County Primary School, Lancashire
Selwyn Junior School, London E4
Snaresbrook Primary School, Wanstead, London E18
South Grove Primary School, Walthamstow, London E17
Southmead Infants School, London SW19
Staining Church of England Primary School, Blackpool
Walton-le-Dale County Primary School, Preston
West Vale County Primary School, Kirkby
Woodridge Primary School, North Finchley, London N12